GCSE EXAM SECRETS

MATHEMATICS

GCSE Exam Secrets

Mathematics

Mark Patmore & Brian Seager

CONTENTS

THIS BOOK AND YOUR GCSE EXAMS

Introduction

This book is designed to help you get better results.

▶ Look at the grade A and C candidates' answers and see if you could have done better.

▶ Try the exam practice questions and then look at the answers.

▶ Make sure you understand why the answers given are correct.

▶ When you feel ready, try the GCSE mock exam papers.

If you perform well on the questions in this book you should do well in the examination. Remember that success in examinations is about hard work, not luck.

What examiners look for

The obvious:

▶ Work which is legible, set out clearly, and easy to follow and understand; that you have used pen, not pencil, except in drawings, and that you have used the appropriate equipment.

▶ That drawings and graphs are neat, and graphs are labelled.

▶ That you always indicate how you obtain your answers.

▶ The right answer!

Exam technique

▶ Start with question 1 and work through the paper in order.

▶ If you cannot answer a question, leave it out and return to it at the end.

▶ For explanation questions, use the mark allocation to guide you on how many points to make.

▶ Make sure you answer the question that has been asked.

▶ Set your work out neatly and logically. Untidy work is not only more difficult for the examiner to read but you could also misread your own figures.

▶ Show all the necessary working so that you can earn the method marks even if you make a numerical slip. You need to convince the examiner that you know what you are doing.

▶ Do not be sloppy with algebraic notation and manipulation, brackets and negatives in particular.

▶ Do rough calculations to check your answers and make sure they are reasonable.

▶ Do not plan to have time left over at the end. If you do, use it usefully. Check you have answered all the questions, check arithmetic and read longer answers to make sure you have not made silly mistakes or missed things out.

See also Top Tips for Exam Success on page 7.

DIFFERENT TYPES OF EXAM QUESTIONS

Understand the question

It is important that you understand what the examiner means when using words like 'State', 'Find' and 'Deduce'? Here is a brief glossary to help you:

Write down, state – no working out or explanation needed.
Calculate, find, show, solve – some working out needed. Include enough working to make your method clear.
Deduce, hence – make use of an earlier answer to establish the result.
Prove – set out a concise logical argument, making the reasons clear.
Sketch – show the general shape of a graph, its relationship with the axes and points of special significance.
Draw – if a graph, plot accurately using graph paper; use geometrical instruments carefully for other diagrams.
Find the exact value – leave in fractions, surds or π. Rounded results from a calculator will not earn the marks.

Multistep questions

Multistep questions require you to obtain the answer to a problem where more than one step is required. Questions which are not multistep are sometimes called **structured**. In these, there may still be more than one step, but each stage is set out in the question. Here is an example.

Structured questions

The diagram shows one end of a railway van.
The roof SQ is a circular arc, centre B, the mid-point of RP.
RP = 2.10 m, PQ = 2.33 m.
Calculate:
(a) the length of BQ [2]
(b) the angle BQP [3]
(c) the length of the arc QS. [3]

Multistep question

Calculate the length of the arc QS. [8]

In the second form of the question, it is necessary to work out the radius of the circle (BQ) and the angle SBQ (twice angle BQP) before finding the length of the arc. The work is exactly the same but in the second case, you are not told what the intermediate steps are. You need to work out the strategy for yourself.

Using a calculator

Half of GCSE Mathematics papers must be answered without the use of calculating aids. This means that either the first paper is non-calculator, or the first section of each paper is non-calculator.
In this book, questions which have to be answered without a calculator are marked with this symbol.
For the mock examination at the end of the book, the first paper is non-calculator.

Algebra

In a Higher Tier GCSE paper, about one-third of the marks will be for algebra. Most of these will be for manipulative algebra, that is expanding brackets, simplifying, factorising, solving equations and inequalities, changing the subject of a formula. Some of the algebra marks will be for graphs, substitution and sequences.

WHAT IS NEEDED TO BE AWARDED A GRADE A IN MATHEMATICS

The following statements are a list of the minimum requirements of those aspects of mathematics that you are expected to know for the award of a grade A on the written examination papers. They are based on the generic descriptors that are used by all examination boards and do not include any requirements that would be covered by coursework.

An grade A candidate should be able to:

▶ Give reasons, justify and explain solutions to problems.

▶ Use mathematical language and symbols in reasoned argument.

▶ Understand rational and irrational numbers.

▶ Determine bounds of intervals.

▶ Understand and use direct and inverse proportion.

▶ Rearrange and manipulate formulae; solve equations; find factors; understand rules of indices; solve simultaneous equations algebraically and graphically; solve other problems graphically.

▶ Use sine, cosine and tangent of angles of any size.

▶ Understand and use Pythagoras' theorem in 2 and 3 dimensions.

▶ Use conditions for congruent triangles in formal geometric proofs.

▶ Calculate lengths of arcs and areas of sectors.

▶ Calculate the surface area of cylinders and the volumes of cones and spheres.

▶ Construct and interpret histograms.

▶ Understand different methods of sampling.

▶ Recognise when and how to use probabilities associated with independent and mutually exclusive events.

What do I need for a grade A*?

Unlike grade A, there are no criteria for the A* grade. You need to get nearly all of the questions right. You should have no weaknesses in any area of the specification. The boundary mark is determined to be the same number of marks above grade A as grade B is below grade A.

HOW TO BOOST YOUR GRADE

Common areas of difficulty

These are the parts of the Higher tier specification which candidates find difficult. You will find help in revising these in *Letts Revise GCSE Mathematics Study Guide*. The references are given in brackets.

▶ Algebra, especially solving equations, inequalities, changing the subject of a formula, algebraic fractions (2.2, 2.7, 2.8, 2.9, 2.10)

▶ Proportion, particularly inverse proportion (2.6)

▶ Reversed percentages, e.g. finding cost before VAT was added (1.5)

▶ Manipulating surds (1.8)

▶ Solving 3-D problems using Pythagoras and trigonometry (3.3, 3.4)

▶ Histograms and frequency density (4.3)

▶ Conditional probability, where the probability of an event depends on what has happened before (4.4)

▶ Vectors (3.9)

Top tips for exam success

▶ Practise all aspects of manipulative algebra, solving equations, rearranging formulae, expanding brackets, factorising, simplifying.

▶ Practise answering questions without the use of a calculator.

▶ Practise answering questions with more than one step to the answer (multistep questions), e.g. finding the radius of a sphere with the same volume as a given cone.

▶ Make your drawings and graphs neat and accurate.

▶ Practise answering questions that ask for an explanation or proof. Your answers should be concise and use mathematical terms where appropriate.

▶ Don't forget to check your answers, especially to see that they are reasonable. The mean height of a group of men will not be 187 metres!

▶ Lay out your working carefully and concisely. Write down the calculations that you are going to make. You usually get marks for showing a correct method.

▶ Know what is on, and what is not on the formula sheet before the examination.

▶ Make sure you can use your calculator efficiently. Write down the figures on your calculator and then make suitable rounding. Don't round the numbers during the calculation. This will often result in an inaccurate answer.

▶ Make sure you have read the question carefully so you give the answer the examiner wants!

CHAPTER 1

Number

To revise this topic more thoroughly, see Chapter 1 in *Letts Revise GCSE Mathematics Study Guide*.

Try this sample GCSE question and then compare your answers with the Grade C and Grade A model answers on the next page. *Do not use a calculator in this question.*

a Find fractions equivalent to these decimals.
Give your answers in their lowest terms.

(i) 0.124

....

.... **[1]**

(ii) 0.$\dot{1}$2$\dot{4}$

....

....

.... **[4]**

b Simplify these, writing each as a simple surd.

(i) $\sqrt{2} \times \sqrt{8}$

.... **[1]**

(ii) $\dfrac{1}{\sqrt{3}}$

.... **[1]**

(iii) $(1 + \sqrt{2})^2$

....

.... **[2]**

(iv) $\dfrac{1}{1 + \sqrt{2}}$

....

.... **[3]**

(Total 12 marks)

These two answers are at grades C and A. Compare which one your answer is closest to and think how you could have improved it.

GRADE C ANSWER

Michael

Correct. ———→ a (i) $0.124 = \dfrac{124}{1000} = \dfrac{62}{500} = \dfrac{31}{250}$ ✓

(ii) $0.1\dot{2}\dot{4} = 0.124124124\ldots$ ←——— Michael has multiplied by 10, which is the right idea but × 1000 is what is needed.

$1.24 = 1.24\ldots$

$= 1.12$ ✗

b (i) $\sqrt{2} \times \sqrt{8} = \sqrt{(2 \times 8)} = \sqrt{16} = 4$ ✓ ←——— This is correct and clearly set out.

No progress towards rationalising the denominator and a classic error, $\frac{1}{3} = 0.3$.

(ii) $\dfrac{1}{\sqrt{3}} = \sqrt{\dfrac{1}{3}} = \sqrt{0.3}$ ✗

(iii) $(1 + \sqrt{2})^2 = 1^2 + (\sqrt{2})^2 = 1 + 2 = 3$ ✗ ←——— Another common error, remember $(a + b)^2 = a^2 + 2ab + b^2$

(iv) ?

2 marks = Grade C answer

Grade booster ⋯⟩ move a C to a B
Michael will struggle to make a C grade making mistakes like this. Other questions will need to be much better than this if he is to succeed. However, much of this question is on work which is higher than C.

GRADE A ANSWER

Leon

Correct. ———→ a (i) $\dfrac{124}{1000} = \dfrac{31}{250}$ ✓

(ii) $F = 0.124124\ldots$

$1000F = 124.124124\ldots$ ✓ ←——— This work is correct and clear.

$999F = 124$ ✓

This fraction will not simplify. ———→ $F = \dfrac{124}{999}$ ✓✓

b (i) $\sqrt{2} \times 2\sqrt{2} = 4$ ✓ ←——— Correct again.

(ii) $\dfrac{\sqrt{3}}{3}$ ✓ ←——— This has clearly been understood.

Silly to lose a mark here for not adding 2 and 1! ———→ (iii) $1 + 2\sqrt{2} + 2$ ✓

(iv) $\dfrac{1 + \sqrt{2}}{(1 + \sqrt{2})^2} = ?$ ✗ ←——— Almost the right idea but multiplying by $1 - \sqrt{2}$ was required.

8 marks = Grade A answer

Grade booster ⋯⟩ move A to A*
Leon clearly understands most of this work and should get a grade A if other questions are as good. However, 2 marks were lost for not following the instructions in the question. With care to avoid such slips, even an A* could be possible.

Try this sample GCSE question and then compare your answers with the Grade C and Grade A model answers on the next page.

1 a John's annual pay is increased from £22 895 to £24 041.
What is the percentage increase?

....

....

....

....

.... **[3]**

b He also received a bonus. After paying tax on it at 22%, he was paid £390.
How much was the bonus?

....

....

....

.... **[3]**

c He managed to save £800, which he invested at 4.5% compound interest.

(i) How much will there be after three years?

....

....

.... **[3]**

(ii) How many years will it be before the amount becomes £1000?

....

....

....

.... **[2]**

(Total 11 marks)

These two answers are at grades C and A. Compare which one your answer is closest to and think how you could have improved it. See Revise Mathematics Guide section 1.5 for further help.

GRADE C ANSWER

Noreen

a
$$\frac{24\,041 - 22\,895}{22\,895} = 0.050054597 \checkmark$$
✓

Correct and sensible rounding, although 5.0% would have been better. →

$$\approx 5\% \checkmark$$

b $\quad 390 \times 1.22 = \pounds 475.80$ ✗ ← *Although a sensible multiplier method is used, this calculation is for a 22% increase, not the reverse of a 22% decrease.*

c (i) $\quad 800 \times \dfrac{4.5}{100} = 36$ ✓

Noreen just gets the first mark for the amount after one year but then uses simple interest. →

In three years $800 + 36 \times 3 = 908$ ✗

(ii) ? ← *Noreen clearly does not understand compound interest.*

4 marks = Grade C answer

> **Grade booster ┈┈> move a C to a B**
> Noreen can do problems involving simple percentages but to be successful at Grade C the competence should be higher than this. The use of multipliers helps to make compound interest or reversed percentage problems more straightforward. This could even lead to a Grade B.

GRADE A ANSWER

Alison

This is correct but it is a risky strategy to only write down the answer, however confident you are that it is right. →

a $\quad 5.0\%$ ✓✓✓

b $\quad 390 \div 0.78$ ✓✓

$\quad\quad = 500$ ✓ ← *This is a better approach. The use of 0.78 earns a mark as does dividing by it.*

This is clearly set out and correct. Although the question does not ask for it, giving the answer to the nearest penny is sensible. →

c (i) $\quad 800 \times (1.045)^3$ ✓✓

$\quad\quad = \pounds 912.93$ ✓

(ii) 3 years ← *The answer is 6 and Alison has forgotten to add in the first three years. Both marks are lost as no method was shown.*

9 marks = Grade A answer

> **Grade booster ┈┈> move A to A***
> This work is below Grade A* standard but those who hope for A* should get it right. Alison clearly does understand what she is doing but has lost valuable marks through lack of care. Even when you are using a calculator, write down what you are going to calculate as well as the answer.

Number

Number

1 a) Write 24 as a product of prime factors.

....

....

.... ②

b) i) Find the lowest common multiple of 24 and 56.

....

.... ①

ii) Find the highest common factor of 24 and 56.

....

.... ①

c) i) Find the highest common factor and the lowest common multiple of 36 and 84.

....

....

.... ④

ii) How did the HCF help you to find the LCM? Explain.

....

.... ①

TOTAL 9

2 The number 450 can be written as $2^a \times 3^b \times 5^c$.
Calculate the values of a, b and c.

....

....

.... ③

TOTAL 3

3 Simplify

a) i) $25^{\frac{1}{2}}$ ii) 3^{-2} iii) 7^0

.... ③

b) Five multiplied by the reciprocal of ten.

.... ①

c) $\dfrac{(3^2)^4}{(3^4)^{-\frac{1}{2}}}$

....

.... ②

TOTAL 6

4 Write as simply as possible.

a) $(3 \times 10^4) \times (2 \times 10^{-2})$

.... ②

b) $(8 \times 10^{-3}) \times (7 \times 10^7)$

.... ②

c) $\dfrac{4.5 \times 10^6}{9 \times 10^{-2}}$

.... ②

TOTAL 6

5 a) Write these numbers in standard form.

i) 530 000 000 ii) 0.000 000 53

.... ②

b) A spacecraft travels at 4×10^7 m/h.
Write this as an ordinary number in km/h.

....

.... ①

TOTAL 3

6 Work out, giving your answers in standard form, correct to 4 significant figures.

a) $63 \times 365.25 \times 24 \times 3600$

....

.... ②

b) $\dfrac{5.73 \times 10^{12}}{3.98 \times 10^4 \times 8.3 \times 10^{-3}}$

....

.... ③

TOTAL 5

7 a) Use index notation to express 144 as a product of prime factors.

....

....

....

.... ③

b) Simplify.

i) $\dfrac{2^6 \times 5^4}{10^3}$ ② ii) $\left(2^8\right)^{\frac{1}{2}}$ ①

....

....

c) Simplify, writing the answers without indices.

i) $64^{-\frac{1}{3}}$ ① ii) $25^{-\frac{3}{2}}$ ① iii) $\dfrac{\left(2^{\frac{1}{2}}\right)^3}{\left(2^{-3}\right)^{\frac{1}{2}}}$ ①

....

....

....

TOTAL 9

8 Work out.

a) $2\frac{3}{4} + 1\frac{3}{5}$

....

.... ③

b) $2\frac{3}{4} \times 1\frac{3}{5}$

....

.... ③

TOTAL 6

9 Work out.

a) $4\frac{1}{4} - 3\frac{2}{3}$

....

.... ③

b) $4\frac{1}{4} \div 3\frac{2}{3}$

....

.... ③

TOTAL 6

10 a) Convert these fractions into decimals.

   i) $\frac{3}{16}$ ①   ii) $\frac{4}{15}$ ②

....

b) Convert these decimals into fractions in their lowest terms.

   i) 0.093 75 ②   ii) $0.\overset{..}{3}\overset{}{6}$ ②

....

....

....

TOTAL 7

11 Two fractions have a mean of $\frac{5}{12}$ and range $\frac{1}{3}$.
Work out the two fractions.

....

....

....

.... ④

TOTAL 4

12 a) Add together $0.1\overset{.}{6}$ and $0.2\overset{.}{6}$, expressing the result as a recurring decimal.

....

.... ②

b) Show the result is correct by converting the decimals into fractions.

....

.... ③

TOTAL 5

13 A jug containing 750 ml of water is put into the freezer.
When frozen, the volume of ice is 810 ml.

Calculate the percentage increase.

....

.... ③

TOTAL 3

14 A dishwasher costs £440, including VAT at 17.5%. What is the cost without VAT?

£440

....

....

....

.... ③

TOTAL 3

15 A 'Supaball' is dropped on the floor from a height of 2 m. Each time it bounces, it rises to 85% of the height from which it fell.

a) How high will it rise after the second bounce?

....

.... ② 2 m

b) After how many bounces will it rise to a height of less than 1 m?

....

....

.... ②

TOTAL 4

16 James invested some money at 4.7% interest for one year. At the end of the year there was £16 437.90.

a) How much had he invested?

....

.... ③

b) The interest rate falls to 3.95%, compound. If he leaves the money in the account, how many years will it be before he has over £20 000?

....

.... ③

TOTAL 6

17 Mr and Mrs Bristow borrowed £150 000 to buy a house.
Every month 0.5% interest is added to the amount they owe at the beginning of the month, but they pay back £800.

a) How much do they owe at the end of two months?

....

.... ③

b) After 6 months, how much do they owe?

....

....

.... ②

TOTAL 5

18 Three friends bought lottery tickets.
They agreed to share any prizes in the ratio of the number of tickets they bought.

a) One week, Sarah bought 6 tickets, Bronwyn 3 and Gail 5.
They won £53 876.
Work out how much each should get.

....

....

....

....

.... ③

b) Another week, Sarah forgot to buy a ticket. The other two shared a £10 prize.
Bronwyn's share was £9.09.
Work out the ratio of the number of tickets they each bought.

....

....

.... ②

TOTAL 5

Number

19 Grey paint can be made by mixing white paint with black paint.

a) Light grey paint uses white and black paint in the ratio 15 : 2.
How many litres of light grey paint will be produced using 500 ml of black paint?

....

....

.... ③

b) Dark grey paint uses white and black paint in the ratio 15 : 4.
Find how much white paint is needed to mix with 500 ml of black for this colour.

....

....

.... ②

TOTAL 5

20 Paving blocks measure 100 mm by 200 mm.

My drive has an area of 125 m².
The pattern of the paving requires red,
blue and grey blocks in the ratio 8 : 4 : 3.

Work out the number of blocks of each colour needed.
Give your answer to a sensible degree of accuracy.

....

....

....

.... ④

TOTAL 4

21 There are deductions from my pay for tax, national insurance and pension contribution.
These are in the ratio 20 : 7 : 6.

a) Last month the tax was £412.
How much was the pension contribution?

....

.... ③

b) The ratio of my pay after deductions to the total deductions is 2 : 1.
My pay after deductions was £1327.
Find how much national insurance I paid.

....

....

....

.... ③

TOTAL 6

22 In an epidemic, the number of new cases is increasing by 32% a week.
At the start, there are 2000 cases.

Work out how many there will be after 4 weeks.

....

....

....

.... ③

TOTAL 3

23 A block of ice is melting.
Each day its mass is 75% of that
on the previous day.
At the start, the mass of ice was 400 kg.

How much ice will there be after 10 days?

....

....

.... ③

TOTAL 3

24 A paving block measures 10.0 cm by 20.0 cm
by 6.0 cm, all lengths correct to the
nearest millimetre.

6.0 cm

20.0 cm

10.0 cm

Find the maximum volume of the block.

....

....

.... ③

TOTAL 3

25 Jo got into a lift with five other people.
Here is the sign in the lift.

On the way up to the twelfth floor,
Jo asked everyone's weight.
Here are the results.

**MAX LOAD
6 persons
or 450 kg**

70   60   85   60   95   80

Assuming they all gave their weights correct to the nearest 5 kg and the safety
limit on the lift is also correct to the nearest 5 kg, work out whether or not the
safety conditions were met. Explain your answer.

....

....

....

.... ⑤

TOTAL 5

26 A train covers a measured kilometre (correct to the nearest metre) in 20.8 s (correct to the nearest 0.1 s).

Give the possible limits on its speed in km/h.

....

....

....

.... ④

TOTAL 4

27 Use approximations to estimate the values of the following expressions.

a) $2\pi\sqrt{\dfrac{47.3}{9.81}}$ ③

b) $\dfrac{0.873 \times 52.6}{0.206}$ ②

....

....

....

TOTAL 5

28 Simplify the following surds, giving your answers in the form $p + q\sqrt{r}$.

a) $(2 + \sqrt{3})^2$

....

.... ②

b) $\dfrac{12}{\sqrt{3}}$

....

.... ②

c) $\dfrac{1}{2 + \sqrt{3}}$

....

....

.... ③

TOTAL 7

29 $a = \sqrt{2}$, $b = \sqrt{8}$, $c = \sqrt{5}$.

Work out the values of these expressions.

a) ab

.... ①

b) $\dfrac{ac}{b}$

.... ②

c) $(a + b)^2$

....

.... ②

TOTAL 5

30 Before a tiler can work out his bill,
he needs to know

- the area to be tiled
- the cost of the tiles per square metre
- how long the job will take.

He makes a profit of 15% on the cost of the tiles.
His labour charge is £20 an hour.
VAT at 17.5% must be added to the total bill.
He deducts 15% for cash.

Work out how much he will charge for laying
tiles on 12 m², with tiles costing £19.63 per m².
The job takes 11 hours and the bill is paid in cash.

....

....

....

....

....

.... ⑤

TOTAL 5

Number

1 a) $2 \times 2 \times 2 \times 3$ or $2^3 \times 3$ ❷

b) i) 168 ❶

ii) 8 or $2 \times 2 \times 2$ ❶

c) i) HCF = 12, LCM $12 \times 7 \times 3 = 252$ ❹

ii) HCF is the repeated factor(s). ❶

EXAMINER'S TIP

When dividing to find factors, be systematic, e.g. start with 2. When no more factors of 2, try 3 and so on.

2 $a = 1, b = 2, c = 2$ ❸

EXAMINER'S TIP

Divide to find the factors as before, then read the indices.

3 a) i) 5 ii) $\frac{1}{9}$ iii) 1 ❸

b) $\frac{1}{2}$ ❶

c) 3^{10} ❷

EXAMINER'S TIP

Remember the negative index is the same as reciprocal.

4 a) 6×10^2 ❷

b) 5.6×10^5 ❷

c) 5×10^7 ❷

EXAMINER'S TIP

Although not requested, give answers in standard form. However, 0.5×10^8 is not wrong in c).

5 a) i) 5.3×10^8 ❶

ii) 5.3×10^{-7} ❶

b) 40 000 ❶

6 a) 1.988×10^9 $(1.988\,1288 \times 10^9)$ ❷

b) 1.735×10^{10} $(1.734\,576\,497 \times 10^{10})$ ❸

EXAMINER'S TIP

In each part you will lose a mark if you do not round to 4 significant figures.

7 a) $2^4 \times 3^2$ ❸

b) i) 40 or $2^3 \times 5$ ❷

ii) 16 or 2^4 ❶

c) i) $\frac{1}{4}$ ❶

ii) $\frac{1}{125}$ ❶

iii) 8 ❶

EXAMINER'S TIP

A fractional index means a root.

8 a) $4\frac{7}{20}$ ❸

b) $4\frac{2}{5}$ ❸

EXAMINER'S TIP

$\frac{22}{5}$ is acceptable in b) but $\frac{88}{20}$ will lose 1 mark.

9 a) $\frac{7}{12}$ ❸

b) $\frac{51}{44}$ or $1\frac{7}{44}$ ❸

EXAMINER'S TIP

When dividing (or multiplying) change the mixed numbers into top-heavy fractions.

10 a) i) 0.1875 ❶

ii) $0.2\dot{6}$ ❷

b) i) $\frac{3}{32}$ ❷

ii) $\frac{4}{11}$ ❷

EXAMINER'S TIP

Take care when dividing down $\dfrac{9375}{100\,000}$ not to lose count of the 5s.

11 $\frac{1}{4}$ and $\frac{7}{12}$ ❹

EXAMINER'S TIP

Rather than guess, you could use algebra to find these fractions, $x + y = \frac{10}{12}, x - y = \frac{4}{12}$

12 a) $0.4\dot{3}$ ❷

b) $\frac{1}{6} + \frac{4}{15} = \frac{26}{60}$ ❸

13 8% ❸

EXAMINER'S TIP

Percentage is based on original volume.

14 £374.47 ❸

EXAMINER'S TIP

Remember to divide by 1.175.

15 a) 1.445 m ❷

b) 5 ❷

EXAMINER'S TIP

Don't forget the first two bounces.

16 a) £15 700 **③**
b) 6 more years **③**

EXAMINER'S TIP

This time, don't add in the first year.

17 a) £149 899.75 **③**
b) £149 696.22 **②**

EXAMINER'S TIP

Careful counting is required in b) as you
× 1.005 and − 800.

18 a) £23 089, £11 545, £19 241 **③**
b) 10 : 1 **②**

EXAMINER'S TIP

It is sensible to give these answers to the
nearest pound.

19 a) 4.25 litres **③**
b) 1875 ml **②**

EXAMINER'S TIP

The answer in a) is the total of black and white
paint.

20 3340, 1670, 1250 **④**

EXAMINER'S TIP

It is sensible to round answers up as if you
round down, there will not be enough blocks.

21 a) £123.60 **③**
b) £140.74 **③**

EXAMINER'S TIP

In b), notice that the deductions are half the
pay after deductions. You need $\frac{7}{33}$ of this.

22 6072 **③**

23 22.5 kg **③**

EXAMINER'S TIP

Remember to multiply by $(0.75)^{10}$.

24 1219 cm³ **③**

EXAMINER'S TIP

The error is 0.5 mm so maximum length is
20.05 cm.

25 No – could be 463 kg to 465 kg **⑤**

EXAMINER'S TIP

The maximum possible error is 2.5 kg on each.

26 172.57… 173.58… **④**

EXAMINER'S TIP

For maximum speed use maximum distance
divided by minimum speed.

27 a) 14 (10 to 15) **③**
b) 200 to 250 **②**

EXAMINER'S TIP

There are fact marks for showing the
approximations you make, so write them down.

28 a) $7 + 4\sqrt{3}$ **②**
b) $4\sqrt{3}$ **②**
c) $2 - \sqrt{3}$ **③**

EXAMINER'S TIP

In c), multiply the top and bottom by $2 - \sqrt{3}$.

29 a) 4 **①**
b) $\dfrac{\sqrt{5}}{2}$ **②**
c) 18 **③**

30 £490.28 **⑤**

CHAPTER 2
Algebra

To revise this topic more thoroughly, see Chapter 2 in *Letts Revise GCSE Mathematics Study Guide*.

Try this sample GCSE question and then compare your answers with the Grade C and Grade A model answers on the next page.

1 a Find the point of intersection of the straight lines with equations

$$y = x + 5$$
$$x + y = 3$$

....

.... **[3]**

b

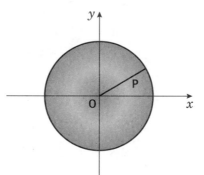

This circle has its centre at the origin and radius 5.

Prove that its equation is

$$x^2 + y^2 = 25.$$

....

.... **[3]**

c Find the points of intersection with the circle of the lines

(i) $y = x + 5$ **(ii)** $x + y = 3$

....

....

....

.... **[9]**

(Total 15 marks)

> These two answers are at grades C and A. Compare which one your answer is closest to and think how you could have improved it.

GRADE C ANSWER

Nasreen

The first line is wrong. It should be $x - y = -5$.

a $\quad y = x + 5$ so $x - y = 5$ ✗

$$x + y = 3$$
$$2x + y - y = 8 \checkmark$$
$$y = 4, \; x = 1$$

Following that error, the rest of the work has been correctly done so there is 1 mark for the method.

b $\quad x^2 + y^2 = (x + y)^2$ ✗

This is not a proof of the result and it contains a serious (and common) error.
$(x + y)^2 = x^2 + 2xy + y^2$

But $x = 1$ and $y = 4$, so $= 25$ – proved.

c (i) ?

(ii) ?

1 mark = Grade C answer

Grade booster ⋯⋗ move a C to a B

Nasreen will be lucky to make a C grade unless other questions are much better than this. Silly mistakes in **a** and **b** have lost her 5 marks. As she did not attempt **c**, perhaps she had not studied the equation of the circle in any depth. High grades can only be achieved if you have covered all the work in the course.

GRADE A ANSWER

Charles

a (i) Substitute $y = x + 5$ in $x + y = 3$ ✓

$$x + x + 5 = 3$$
$$2x = -2, \text{ so } x = -1 \checkmark$$
$$y = x + 5 = 4 \checkmark$$
The point is $(-1, 4)$

This is well set out and uses the method of substitution, which is most appropriate as one equation is in the form $y =$.

b $\quad$ This is true by Pythagoras

This is not a proof of the result.

c (i) $\quad x^2 + (x + 5)^2 = 25$ ✓

$$2x^2 + 10x + 25 = 25$$
$$2x^2 + 10x = 0 \checkmark$$
$$x + 5 = 0, \text{ so } x = -5 \text{ and } y = 0 \checkmark$$

The start is correct, substituting again for y, and the quadratic is right.

However, 2 marks have been lost by not factorising and finding both roots.

(ii) $\quad x + y = 3$ gives $y = 3 - x$ ✓

$$x^2 + (3 - x)^2 = 25$$
$$2x^2 - 6x + 9 = 25$$
$$2x^2 - 6x - 16 = 0 \checkmark$$
$$x^2 - 3x - 8 = 0$$
$$x = \frac{3 \pm \sqrt{9 - 4 \times -8}}{2} = 4.70 \text{ or } -1.70 \checkmark$$
$$y \text{ is } 3 - x = -1.70 \text{ or } 4.70 \checkmark$$

This is a completely correct method with correct solutions to the equation.

However, the last mark is lost as Charles has not made clear that the points are $(4.7, -1.7)$ and $(-1.7, 4.7)$. The values must be paired.

10 marks = Grade A answer

Grade booster ⋯⋗ move A to A*

Charles has scored quite well on this question and, if other answers are as good, will probably be awarded an A grade. If he wants an A*, however, he will have to avoid errors like losing a root of the quadratic by division. He will also need to understand what is required for a proof. In this case, if P has coordinates (x, y), then a right-angled triangle is formed with sides x, y, 5. Applying Pythagoras gives the result. Make sure you state the reasons.

Try this sample GCSE question and then compare your answers with the Grade C and Grade A model answers on the next page.

Solve these equations.

a $3x - 11 = 2(5 - x)$

....

....

....

.... **[3]**

b $x^2 - 3x - 40 = 0$

....

....

....

.... **[3]**

c $\dfrac{3}{x-2} + \dfrac{2}{x-3} = 1$

....

....

....

....

....

....

....

....

....

.... **[6]**

(Total 12 marks)

GRADE C ANSWER

Bill

a
$$3x - 11 = 10 - 2x \checkmark$$
$$5x - 11 = 10 \checkmark$$
$$5x = 21$$
$$x = 4\tfrac{1}{5} \checkmark$$

Completely correct. This is a Grade C question.

b
$$(x - 3)(x - 4) \quad 8 \times 5 = 40$$
$$(x + 3)(x + 4)$$
$$(x - 5)(x + 8) = 0 \enspace ✗$$
$$x = 5 \text{ or } x = -8 \checkmark\checkmark$$

The 8 and 5 are correct but these factors give $x^2 + 3x - 40$.

The solutions are right for Bill's factors, so earn two marks.

c
$$\frac{3}{x - 2} + \frac{2}{x - 3} = 1 \enspace ?$$

No attempt but this is A* work.

5 marks = Grade C answer

Grade booster ⋯⋗ move a C to a B
Continuing like this, Bill will get a good grade C and might make B if he avoids errors like this one in part **b**. He clearly needs more practice in factorising quadratics.

GRADE A ANSWER

Eileen

a
$$3x - 11 = 2(5 - x)$$
$$5x = 21 \checkmark\checkmark$$
$$x = 4\tfrac{1}{5} \checkmark$$

Completely correct.

b
$$x^2 - 3x - 40 = 0$$
$$\text{Try } 2 \times 20 ✗, \enspace 4 \times 10 ✗, \enspace 5 \times 8 \checkmark \enspace \checkmark$$
$$(x - 5)(x + 8) ✗$$
$$(x + 5)(x - 8) \checkmark \enspace \checkmark$$
$$x = -5 \text{ or } 8 \checkmark$$

This is Grade B work, so a Grade A candidate would be expected to get this right.

c
$$\frac{3}{x - 2} + \frac{2}{x - 3} = 1$$
$$\text{Common denominator } (x - 2)(x - 3) \checkmark$$
$$\frac{3(x - 3) + 2(x - 2)}{(x - 2)(x - 3)} = 1$$
$$\frac{5x - 13}{(x - 2)(x - 3)} = 1 \checkmark$$

All correct to this point and well laid out!

$$\text{Therefore } 5x - 13 = 1 ✗$$
$$x = 2\tfrac{3}{5} ✗$$

Here Eileen 'forgot' the denominator, as though it was 0 rather than 1 on the right.

8 marks = Grade A answer

Grade booster ⋯⋗ move A to A*
The last part is difficult at Grade A, so Eileen may still get this grade if other work is up to the standard. To be awarded A* you need to be able to solve equations like this last one. Eileen should have multiplied each side by the denominator and rearranged the quadratic for solution.

Algebra

1 Simplify these expressions.

a) $a^2 \times a^5$

.... ①

b) $\dfrac{a^2}{a^5}$

.... ①

c) $3ab^2 \times 2a^3b$

....

.... ②

d) $\dfrac{8a^3b^4}{2a^4b^3}$

....

.... ②

e) $(3a^2b^3)^2$

....

.... ②

f) $\left(\dfrac{ab^3}{a^3b}\right)^{\frac{1}{2}}$

....

....

.... ②

TOTAL 10

2 The frequency, f, of a radio signal is inversely proportional to its wavelength, w.

a) Write this using the $\propto$ symbol and as a formula.

....

....

....

.... ②

b) When the frequency is 198, the wavelength is 1500. Find:

i) the wavelength for a frequency of 720

....

....

.... ②

ii) the frequency for a wavelength of 3.3.

....

....

.... ②

TOTAL 6

3   Match these proportion relationships to the graphs.

a) $y \propto x$ b) $y \propto x^2$ c) $y \propto \dfrac{1}{x}$ b) $y \propto \dfrac{1}{x^2}$

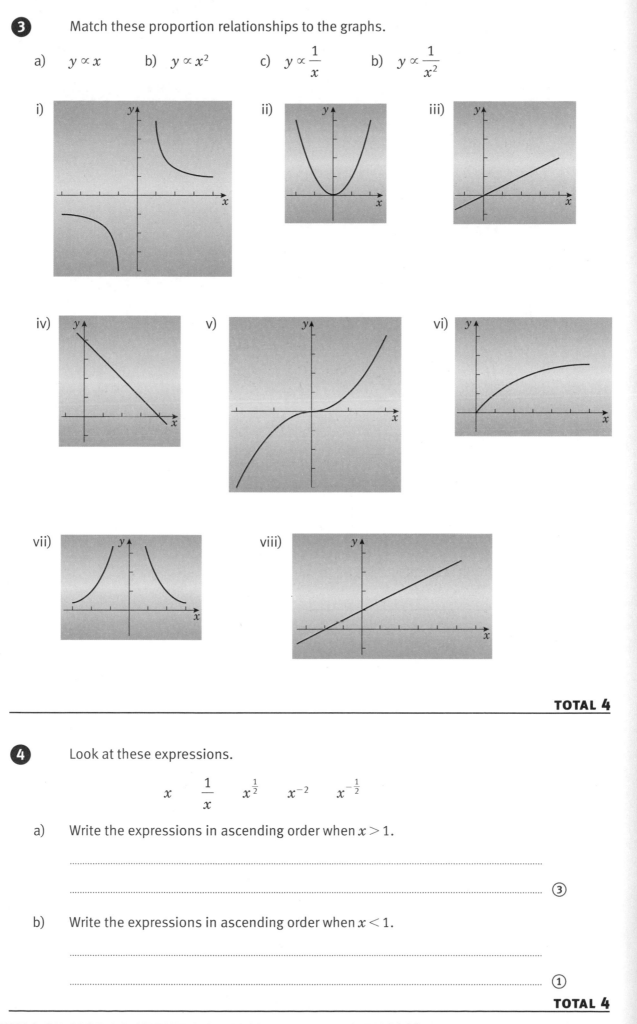

i)   ii)   iii)

iv)   v)   vi)

vii)   viii)

TOTAL 4

4   Look at these expressions.

$$x \qquad \frac{1}{x} \qquad x^{\frac{1}{2}} \qquad x^{-2} \qquad x^{-\frac{1}{2}}$$

a)   Write the expressions in ascending order when $x > 1$.

....

.... ③

b)   Write the expressions in ascending order when $x < 1$.

....

.... ①

TOTAL 4

Algebra

5 a) Expand the brackets and simplify where possible.

    i) $3x(5 - 4x)$

                                             ①

    ii) $(3x + 2)(5 - 4x)$

                                             ②

b) Factorise these expressions.

    i) $2x^2 - 4x$

        ②

    ii) $x^2 - 7x + 12$

        ②

    iii) $6x^2 + 5x - 4$

        ②

TOTAL 9

6 Solve these equations.

a) $\frac{1}{2}(x - 3) = 2x + 1$

        ③

b) $\dfrac{x - 1}{2} = \dfrac{x - 2}{3}$

        ③

TOTAL 6

7 A rectangle has one side four times as long as the other side. Its area is 9 cm².

Use algebra to find its perimeter.

....

....

....

....

....

....

.... ④

TOTAL 4

8 The angles of a quadrilateral are marked on the diagram.

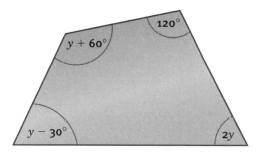

Form an equation in y and solve it to find the angles of the quadrilateral.

....

....

....

....

....

....

....

.... ④

TOTAL 4

ANSWERS ON PAGE 44 ANSWERS ON PAGE 44 ANSWERS ON PAGE 44 ANSWERS ON PAGE 44

9 Solve these equations.

a) $\frac{1}{3}(3 - x) = 2(3x - 1)$

....

....

....

....③

b) $\frac{3x}{10} = 150$

....

....

....②

TOTAL 5

10 $\frac{1}{f} = \frac{1}{u} + \frac{1}{v}$

a) Make f the subject of the formula.

....

....

....

....

....②

b) Make v the subject of the formula.

....

....

....

....

....②

TOTAL 4

11 $P = V(1 + t^2)$

a) Make V the subject of the formula.

....

....①

b) Make t the subject of the formula.

....

....

....③

TOTAL 4

Algebra

12 A cylinder has circumference C and height h.

a) Find a formula for its volume V.

....

....

....

....

.... ④

b) Make C the subject of the formula.

....

....

.... ②

TOTAL 6

13 $$s = \frac{p}{100(q-p)}$$

Make p the subject of the formula.

....

....

....

....

....

.... ④

TOTAL 4

14 Solve these simultaneous equations using algebra.

$$x + 4y = 0$$
$$3x - 2y = -7$$

....

....

....

....

....

....

.... ③

TOTAL 3

15 Use a graphical method to solve these equations simultaneously.

$$x - y + 1 = 0$$
$$2x + y - 6 = 0$$

④

TOTAL 4

16 a) Solve these equations simultaneously.

$$x + 2y = 5$$
$$x^2 + y^2 = 36$$

....

....

....

....

....

.... ⑤

b) Give a geometrical interpretation of the result.

....

.... ②

TOTAL 7

17 Use an algebraic method to find the point of intersection of the lines

$$2x + 3y = 7 \quad \text{and} \quad 3x - 2y = 23\tfrac{1}{2}.$$

....

....

....

....

....

....

....

.... ④

TOTAL 4

18 Solve these inequalities.

a) $3x - 5 < 10$

....

....

.... ②

b) $6 - 4x \geqslant 2x - 3$

....

....

.... ②

c) $x^2 < 100$

....

....

.... ②

TOTAL 6

19 a)   Show these inequalities on a graph.

$$y \geqslant 2x - 1 \qquad x + y \leqslant 5$$

④

b)   Show by shading the region which represents the solution set of

$$x \geqslant 0, y \geqslant 2x - 1, x + y \leqslant 5.$$

②

c)   What is the largest value of x in the region?

.... ①

TOTAL 7

20 a)   Factorise

$$x^2 - 2x - 35.$$

....

....

.... ②

b)   Hence solve the equation

$$x^2 - 2x - 35 = 0.$$

....

.... ①

c)   Hence solve the inequality

$$x^2 - 2x - 35 \leqslant 0.$$

....

....

.... ②

TOTAL 5

21 Use trial and improvement to find the negative root of the equation
$$x^3 - 3x^2 + 5 = 0.$$
Show all the outcomes of your trials and give the answer correct to one decimal place.

....

....

....

....

....

.... ④

TOTAL 4

22 a) The expression
$$2x^2 + 6x - 1$$
may be written as $a(x + b)^2 + c$.
Find the values of a, b and c.

....

....

....

.... ③

b) Hence solve the equation $2x^2 + 6x - 1 = 0$.

....

....

.... ③

TOTAL 6

23 Solve these equations.

a) $2x^2 + 5x - 12 = 0$

....

....

.... ③

b) $2x^2 + 5x - 11 = 0$

....

....

.... ③

TOTAL 6

24 Solve the equation

$$\frac{1}{2x + 1} - \frac{1}{x + 2} = 1$$

⑥

TOTAL 6

25 Find the nth term of each of these sequences.

a) 3, 5, 7, 9, 11, …

②

b) 1, 4, 9, 16, 25, …

①

c) Hence find the nth term of the sequence

4, 9, 16, 25, …

②

TOTAL 5

26 a) Find the *n*th term of the sequence

$$1 \times 2, \ 2 \times 3, \ 3 \times 4, \ 4 \times 5, \ 5 \times 6, \ \ldots$$

....

....

.... ②

b) Explain why this sequence has the same *n*th term.

$$(1 + 1), \ (2 + 4), \ (3 + 9), \ (4 + 16), \ (5 + 25), \ \ldots$$

....

.... ②

TOTAL 4

27 a) i) Find the gradient of the straight line shown on the graph.

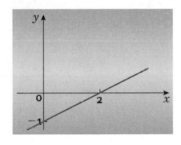

....

....

.... ②

ii) Find the equation of the straight line.

....

....

.... ②

b) i) Find the equation of the line through 0 parallel to the line in part a).

....

....

.... ②

ii) Find the equation of the line through 0 perpendicular to the line in part a).

....

....

.... ②

TOTAL 8

28   Water is poured into these containers at the same constant rate.

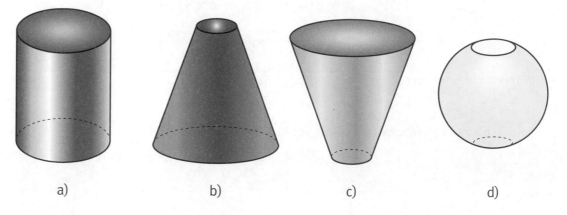

a)   b)   c)   d)

These graphs show the depth of water against time.
Match each container to a graph.

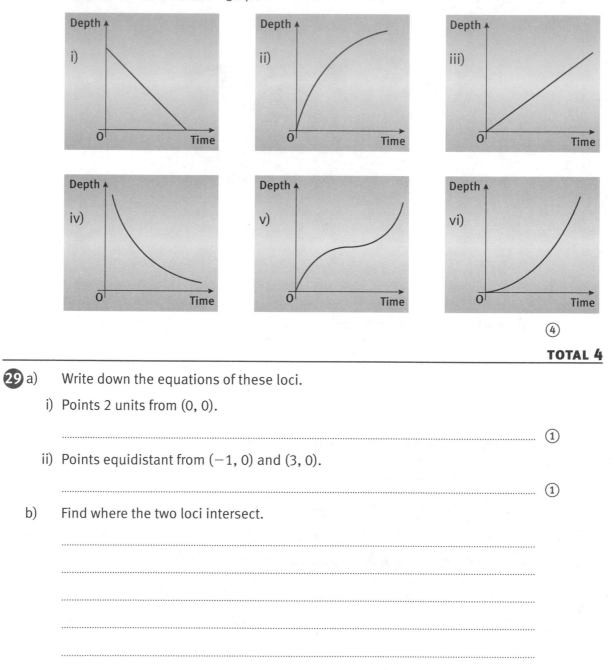

④

TOTAL 4

29 a)   Write down the equations of these loci.

     i)   Points 2 units from $(0, 0)$.

.... ①

     ii)   Points equidistant from $(-1, 0)$ and $(3, 0)$.

.... ①

   b)   Find where the two loci intersect.

....

....

....

....

....

.... ④

TOTAL 6

30   Draw the graph of

$$y = x^3 - 3x + 2,$$

for values of x from -2 to 2.

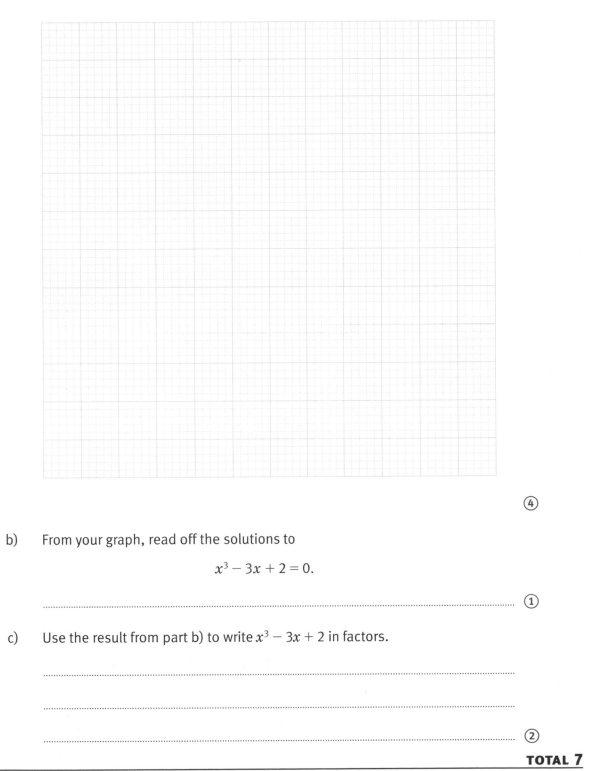

④

b)   From your graph, read off the solutions to

$$x^3 - 3x + 2 = 0.$$

.... ①

c)   Use the result from part b) to write $x^3 - 3x + 2$ in factors.

....

....

.... ②

TOTAL 7

31 This is the graph of

$$y = x^3 + 4x^2 - 3.$$

a) Find the roots of the equation $x^3 + 4x^2 - 3 = 0$.

.... ②

b) By drawing suitable straight lines on the graph, solve these equations.

i) $x^3 + 4x^2 - 4 = 0$

....

.... ②

ii) $x^3 + 4x^2 + x - 2 = 0$

....

....

.... ③

TOTAL 7

32 The sketch graph shows $y = f(x)$.

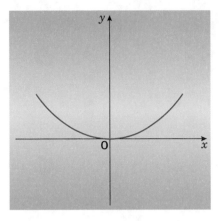

Sketch the graphs of

a) $y = f(2x)$

②

b) $y = f(x) + 1$

②

c) $y = f(x + 1)$

②

d) $y = 2f(x)$

②

TOTAL 8

Algebra

1 a) a^7 ❶ b) a^{-3} ❶
c) $6a^4b^3$ ❷ d) $4a^{-1}b$ or $\dfrac{4b}{a}$ ❷
e) $9a^4b^6$ ❷ f) $\dfrac{b}{a}$ or $a^{-1}b$ ❷

EXAMINER'S TIP

Remember $(b^3)^2$ is b^6.

2 a) $f \propto \dfrac{1}{w}$; $f = \dfrac{k}{w}$ ❷
b) i) 412.5 ❷ ii) 90 000 ❷

EXAMINER'S TIP

It may be easier to use $fw = k$ ($= 297\,000$ in this case).

3 a) iii); b) ii); c) i); d) vii) ❹

4 a) $x^{-2}, \dfrac{1}{x}, x^{-\frac{1}{2}}, x^{\frac{1}{2}}, x$ ❸
b) $x, x^{\frac{1}{2}}, x^{-\frac{1}{2}}, \dfrac{1}{x}, x^{-2}$ ❶

EXAMINER'S TIP

Notice that b) is the reverse order from a).

5 a) i) $15x - 12x^2$ ❶
ii) $10 + 7x - 12x^2$ ❷
b) i) $2x(x - 2)$ ❷
ii) $(x - 3)(x - 4)$ ❷
iii) $(3x + 4)(2x - 1)$ ❷

EXAMINER'S TIP

Take care with the signs. Multiply out as a check.

6 a) $x = -1\frac{2}{3}$ ❸ b) $x = -1$ ❸

EXAMINER'S TIP

Signs again!

7 15 cm ❹

EXAMINER'S TIP

Let the short side be y cm, $4y \times y = 9$. Solve the equation.

8 $4y + 150 = 360$; $y = 52\frac{1}{2}$;
$120°, 105°, 112\frac{1}{2}°, 22\frac{1}{2}°$ ❹

EXAMINER'S TIP

You must write down the equation.

9 $x = \frac{9}{19}$ ❸ b) $x = 500$ ❷

EXAMINER'S TIP

In b), don't be tempted to divide by 10.

10 a) $f = \dfrac{uv}{u + v}$ ❷ b) $v = \dfrac{uf}{u - f}$ ❷

EXAMINER'S TIP

Combine the two fractions first.

11 a) $V = \dfrac{P}{1 + t^2}$ ❶ b) $t = \sqrt{\dfrac{P}{V} - 1}$ ❸

EXAMINER'S TIP

Isolate the t^2 before taking the square root. It could be positive or negative.

12 a) $V = \dfrac{C^2h}{4\pi}$ ❹ b) $C = \sqrt{\dfrac{4\pi V}{h}}$ ❷

EXAMINER'S TIP

Find r (the radius) first.
$r = \dfrac{c}{2\pi}$

13 $p = \dfrac{100sq}{1 + 100s}$ ❹

EXAMINER'S TIP

Notice that p appears twice. These must be collected.

14 $x = -2, y = \frac{1}{2}$ ❸

15 $x = 1.7, y = 2.7$ (exact $1\frac{2}{3}, 2\frac{2}{3}$) ❹

EXAMINER'S TIP

From a graph you cannot expect greater accuracy.

16 a) $x = -3.98, y = 4.49$; $x = 5.98, y = -0.49$ ❺
b) Points of intersection of line $x + 2y = 5$ with circle radius 6, centre 0 ❷

EXAMINER'S TIP

The easiest way to start is substituting $x = 5 - 2y$

17 $(6\frac{1}{2}, -2)$ ❹

18 a) $x < 5$ **②**   b) $x \leq 1\frac{1}{2}$ **②**   c) $-10 < x < 10$ **②**

EXAMINER'S TIP

> Remember the negative square root in c).

19 a) b)

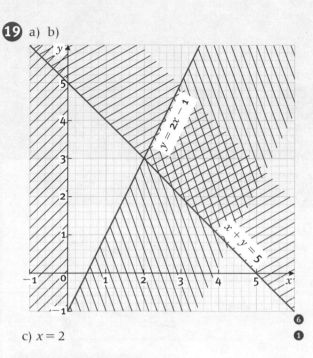

c) $x = 2$ **①**

EXAMINER'S TIP

> It is clearer to shade the unwanted regions.

20 a) $(x - 7)(x + 5)$ **②**   b) $x = 7$ or $x = -5$ **①**
c) $-5 \leq x \leq 7$ **②**

EXAMINER'S TIP

> For c), one bracket must be positive and one negative.

21 $x = -1.1$ **④**

EXAMINER'S TIP

> You should show the root is nearer to -1.1 than -1.2

22 a) $a = 2$, $b = 1\frac{1}{2}$, $c = -5\frac{1}{2}$ **③**
b) 0.16, -3.16 or $-1\frac{1}{2} \pm \frac{1}{2}\sqrt{11}$ **③**

23 a) $1\frac{1}{2}$, -4 **③**   b) 1.41, -3.91 **③**

EXAMINER'S TIP

> Try to factorise first

24 -0.18, -2.82 **⑥**

25 a) $2n + 1$ **②**   b) n^2 **①**
c) $n^2 + 2n + 1$ or $(n + 1)^2$ **②**

26 a) $n(n + 1)$ **②**
b) $n(n + 1) = n^2 + n$ **②**

EXAMINER'S TIP

> You should work with nth terms to show the result.

27 a) i) $\frac{1}{2}$ **②**   ii) $y = \frac{1}{2}x - 1$ **②**
b) i) $y = \frac{1}{2}x$ **②**   ii) $y = -2x$ **②**

EXAMINER'S TIP

> You can have alternative forms for the equation, e.g. $2y = x$.

28 a) iii); b) vi); c) ii); d) v) **④**

29 a) i) $x^2 + y^2 = 4$ **①**   ii) $x = 1$ **①**
b) $(1, \sqrt{3})$, $(1, -\sqrt{3})$ **④**

EXAMINER'S TIP

> A sketch will help to spot quick solutions.

30 a)

④
b) -2, 1 **①**
c) $(x + 2)(x - 1)^2$ **②**

31 Solutions from graph
a) -3.8, -1, 0.8 **②**
b) i) -3.7, -1.2, 0.9 (read at $y = 1$) **②**
ii) -3.6, -1, 0.6 (read at $y = x - 1$) **③**

EXAMINER'S TIP

> Draw the lines $y = 1$ and $y = x - 1$ on the graph.

32 a) Graph half width **②**
b) Translated up 1 **②**
c) Translated 1 left **②**
d) Double height **②**

Algeba

Shape, space and measures

To revise this topic more thoroughly, see Chapter 3 in *Letts Revise GCSE Mathematics Study Guide*.

Try this sample GCSE question and then compare your answers with the Grade C and Grade A model answers on the next page.

1   The diagram shows a parallelogram ABCD.

AB = 10 cm and BC = 16 cm.
Points P, Q, R, S are fixed on AB, BC, CD
and DA respectively, so that
AP = BQ = CR = DS = 3 cm.

Prove, giving reasons, that

a   triangle APS is congruent to triangle CRQ

....

....

....

....

....

.... **[3]**

b   the quadrilateral PQRS is a parallelogram.

....

....

....

....

....

.... **[3]**

(Total 6 marks)

These two answers are at grades C and A. Compare which one your answer is closest to and think how you could have improved it.

GRADE C ANSWER

Lucy

Although this relationship is derived and earns one mark this is a long way of doing so – the relationship should have been known however.

a Angle PAS + Angle PBQ = 180°

Angle QCR + Angle PBQ = 180°

Therefore Angle PAS = Angle QCR ✓

Angle ASP = angle RQC

Angle APS = angle CRQ ✗

No reasons are given for these two statements and so no mark. She also assumes that PS is parallel to QR – but this has yet to be established!

Proving that two triangles are congruent depends on proving that, or using the fact that, at least one side in each triangle is equal. What has happened here is that Lucy has used the condition for similarity and therefore gains no marks.

therefore the triangles are congruent. ✗

b Because AS = QC and AP = CR then PS = QR

also PS is parallel to QR by symmetry

Therefore PQRS is a parallelogram ✗

These facts are given but it is not valid to then state that this means PQ = QR. The symmetry argument is incomplete and therefore inconclusive – more information about why symmetry is present is needed. No marks are gained in this part.

1 mark = Grade C answer

> **Grade booster ⋯⋙ move a C to a B**
> Lucy will need to improve her understanding of proof. She will have to appreciate that (i) only facts that are given or proved may be used and (ii) reasons/explanations for statements must be provided – had she done this, for example in part **a**, she would have gained 1 more mark. She also needs to learn the difference between similarity and congruence.

GRADE A ANSWER

Asif

a AP = CR ✓

angle PAS = angle QCR (interior opposite angles of parallelogram) ✓

The correct reasons are given here so the maximum marks for this part are gained.

AS = QC

Therefore triangle APS is congruent to ✓ triangle CRQ (SAS)

b Because triangle APS is congruent to triangle CPQ then angle ASP = angle CQR ✓

Therefore PS is parallel to QR

Therefore PQRS is a prallelogram ✗

(1 pair of opposite sides are parallel.)

Only one valid deduction, the angles being equal, is made from the fact that the triangles are congruent and gains one mark. The fact that PS is parallel to QR is not explained or proved; this is insufficient proof for a parallelogram – the pair of opposite sides must also be equal and this fact needs establishing here.

4 marks = Grade A answer

> **Grade booster ⋯⋙ move A to A***
> Asif has gained full marks in part **a** but lost marks in part **b** through not including a reason why PS is parallel to QR. (The reason is because AS is parallel to QC and angle ASP = angle CQR.)

Shape, space and measures

Shape, space and measures

1 ABC is an isosceles triangle. AC = BC and X and Y are points on AC and BC so that CX = CY.

Prove triangle CXB is congruent to triangle CYA.

....

....

....

.... ②

TOTAL 2

2 In this figure DX = XC, DV = ZC, AB is parallel to DC.

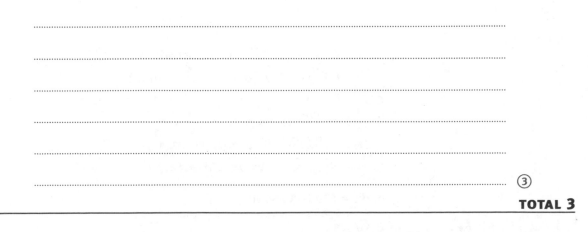

Prove triangle DBZ is congruent to triangle CAV.

....

....

....

....

....

.... ③

TOTAL 3

3 These two triangles are congruent.

a) Write down the lengths of   side a .... cm

                               side b .... cm   ②

b) Write down the sizes of angles x .... °

                                 y .... °

                                 z .... °   ③

TOTAL 5

---

4 ABCD is a rhombus. AB = BC = CD = DA.
AB is parallel to DC, BC is parallel to AD.

a) Prove that
   i) triangles ABX and CDX are congruent

....

....

....

.... ③

   ii) triangles ADX and CBX are congruent.

....

....

....

.... ②

b) Prove that X is the midpoint of DB and AC and hence that the diagonals of a rhombus intersect at right angles.

....

....

....

....

.... ③

TOTAL 8

5 In the diagram, AB = AC, angle BAC = 40° and CE = CF.

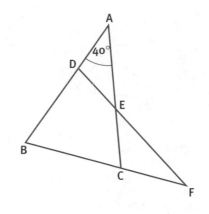

Find angle ADE.

.... ②

TOTAL 2

6 In this diagram, CD is the bisector of angle ACB and AE is parallel to DC.

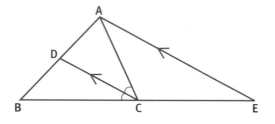

Prove that AC = CE.

....

....

....

....

....

.... ③

TOTAL 3

7 In this diagram, PQ is parallel to SR, SP = SR, angle SPR = 66° and angle PQS = 22°.

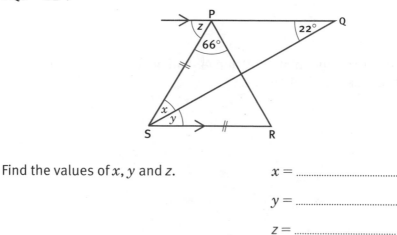

Find the values of x, y and z.

$x = $ ....

$y = $ ....

$z = $ .... ③

TOTAL 3

8 ABCD is a quadrilateral. Angle CBA = 70°, angle BAD = 80° and angle ADC = 130°.
CA bisects angle DCB.

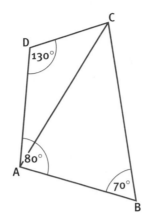

Prove that triangle CAB is isosceles.

....

....

....

.... ③

TOTAL 3

9 Calculate the length of AB in this diagram.

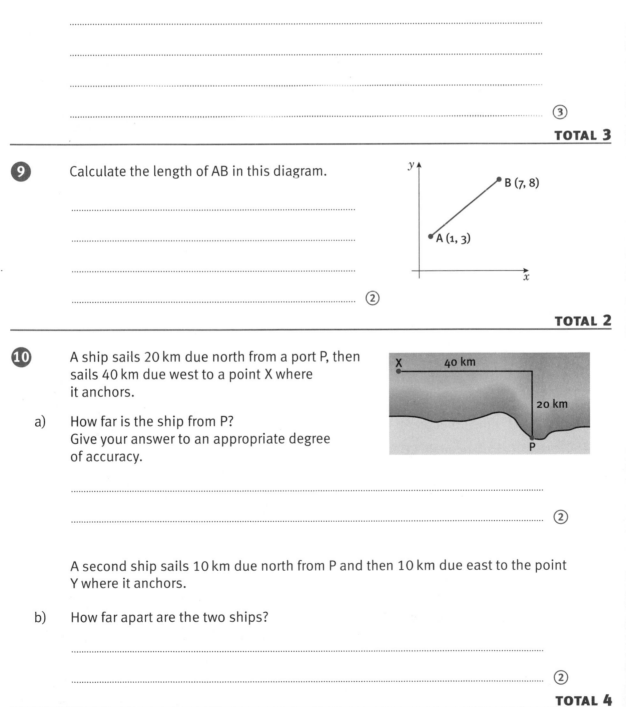

....

....

....

.... ②

TOTAL 2

10 A ship sails 20 km due north from a port P, then
sails 40 km due west to a point X where
it anchors.

a) How far is the ship from P?
Give your answer to an appropriate degree
of accuracy.

....

.... ②

A second ship sails 10 km due north from P and then 10 km due east to the point
Y where it anchors.

b) How far apart are the two ships?

....

.... ②

TOTAL 4

Shape, space and measures

11 The diagonal of a rectangle is 2 cm greater than the length of the rectangle, *l* cm.
The width of the rectangle is 8 cm.
Calculate the value of *l*.

....

....

.... ③

TOTAL 3

12 A, B, C are three points on horizontal ground.
A is 1000 m due west of C and B is 800 m due south of C.
CT is a vertical television mast.

The angle of elevation of T from A is 15°.

a) Find the height of the mast.

....

.... ①

b) Find the angle of elevation from B.

....

.... ①

P is the point on AB which is nearest to C.

c) Calculate angle CBA.

....

.... ①

d) Calculate the distance CP.

....

.... ①

e) Calculate the angle of elevation of T from P.

....

.... ①

TOTAL 5

ANSWERS ON PAGE **66** ANSWERS ON PAGE **66** ANSWERS ON PAGE **66** ANSWERS ON PAGE **66**

13 The diagram shows two circles inside a square of side 10 cm.
The circle, centre P, has radius r.
The circle, centre Q, has radius 2 cm.

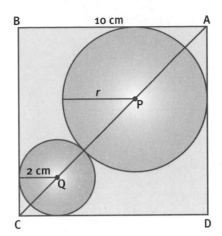

a) Show that $AP = r\sqrt{2}$.

....

....

....

.... ③

b) Write down expressions for AC, PQ, QC.

....

....

.... ③

c) Hence show that $r = \dfrac{8\sqrt{2} - 2}{\sqrt{2} + 1}$

....

....

.... ④

TOTAL 10

Shape, space and measures

14 Points A, B and C lie on a circle centre O.
AB = 20 cm, BC = 15 cm and angle CBA = 30°.

a) Calculate the length of AC.

....

....

....

.... ②

b) Hence calculate angle BAC.

....

....

....

.... ②

c) Prove that triangle AOC is equilateral.

....

....

.... ②

d) Calculate angle OCB.

.... ②

TOTAL 8

15 P and Q are two positions, 1000 m apart on horizontal
ground, which are used to observe hot air balloons
during a race.

The angle of elevation of a balloon
from P is 21° and from Q is 25°.

Calculate the height of the balloon.
Give your answer correct to 3 s.f.

....

....

....

....

.... ④

TOTAL 4

16 The sides of the quadrilateral ABCD touch
the circle at P, Q, R and S.

Prove that AB + CD = BC + DA.
Give the reasons for each statement that you make.

....

....

....

....

....

.... ④

TOTAL 4

17 In the diagram, AT and CT are tangents, B is a point on the circle,
angle CAB = 40° and angle BAT = 32°.

a) i) Calculate the size of angle ACB. Give a reason for your answer.

.... ①

ii) What is the size of angle BCT?

.... ①

iii) What is the size of angle CTA?

.... ①

b) Calculate the length of AC.

....

....

.... ③

TOTAL 6

Shape, space and measures

18 ABCD is a cyclic quadrilateral. Angle BAC = 40°, Angle BPC = 105° and angle ADB = 30°.

Calculate the size of angle BCD.

....

....

.... ③

TOTAL 3

19 The volume of a rectangular block of candle wax is 375 cm³.
It has a length of 20 cm and a width of 7.5 cm.

a) Calculate the height of the block.

....

.... ①

The block is melted down and 125 cm³ of the wax is poured into each of three separate moulds. The first mould is a cube, the second a cylinder of height 12 cm and the third mould is a pyramid with a square base of side x cm and height $2x$ cm.

b) Calculate

i) the length of the edge of the cube

.... ①

ii) the radius of the cylinder

....

....

....

.... ②

iii) the value of x.

....

....

....

.... ②

TOTAL 5

20 A rectangular block of metal has a length of 60 cm, a width of 30 cm and a height of 20 cm.

a) Calculate
   i) the volume of the block

   .... ①

   ii) the total surface area of the block.

   ....

   .... ③

   A similar block has length, width and height all 35% greater than the first block.

b) Calculate
   i) the volume of the enlarged block

   ....

   .... ②

   ii) the total surface area of the enlarged block.

   ....

   .... ②

   TOTAL 8

21 In the following expressions, a, b, c, d are lengths.
Indicate which expressions might represent area and which might represent volume.

   i) $2(a + b)$

   ii) $\frac{1}{3}abc$

   iii) $\frac{1}{2}ab \cos\theta$

   iv) $4\sqrt{ab + bc + cd}$

   v) $\frac{1}{3}(a^2b + ab^2)$

   vi) $3a^2$

   Area .... Volume ....

   ....

   .... ③

   TOTAL 3

22 The diagram shows four triangles, T1, T2, T3, T4

Describe fully the single transformation that maps

a) T1 onto T2

....

.... ②

b) T1 onto T3

....

.... ②

T1 is mapped onto T4 by an enlargement.

c) Find

i) the scale factor of the enlargement .... ①

ii) the coordinates of the centre of this enlargement. .... ①

TOTAL 6

23 A, B and C are the vertices of an equilateral triangle.

P, Q, R are the midpoints of sides BC, CA, AB respectively.
O is the centre of the triangle.

a) Triangle ABC is rotated anticlockwise through 120° about centre O.
Which points are the images of A, B and C after the rotation?

.... ①

b) Describe the transformation that will map A onto B, B onto A, and Q onto P.

.... ②

c) i) Describe the transformation that will map R to Q, C to B, *but not* B to C.

.... ②

ii) To which point will B be mapped? .... ①

d) Triangle ABC is enlarged with a scale factor of 2 using A as the centre of enlargement.

What are the images of i) Q .... ①

ii) R? .... ①

TOTAL 8

24 'It Sticks' glue is available in two sizes of tubes.
The tubes are similar.

8 cm

12 cm

The larger size contains 50 cm³ of glue.
How much glue is in the smaller size.

....

....

.... ②

TOTAL 2

25 A model is made of a car ferry using a scale of 1:60.
Complete the following table. Give your answers in the units indicated.

	Car ferry	Scale model	
Angle between flag pole and deck	85°	°	①
Height of funnel	8 m	cm	①
Volume of a typical passenger cabin	6.8 m³	cm³	②

....

....

TOTAL 4

Shape, space and measures

26 In this diagram, $\overrightarrow{OA} = \mathbf{a}$, $\overrightarrow{OC} = 3\mathbf{a}$ and $\overrightarrow{OB} = 2\mathbf{b}$.

E is the midpoint of AB and $BF = \frac{1}{4} BC$.

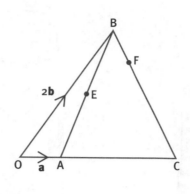

a) Express in terms of **a** and **b**

  i) $\overrightarrow{AB}$ .... ①

  ii) $\overrightarrow{AE}$ .... ①

  iii) $\overrightarrow{OE}$ .... ①

  iv) $\overrightarrow{OF}$ ....

  .... ①

b) Deduce two facts about O, E, and F.

  ....

  .... ②

TOTAL 6

27 OABC is a parallelogram and $\overrightarrow{OA} = 3\mathbf{a}$ and $\overrightarrow{OC} = 2\mathbf{c}$.

D is the midpoint of AB, E divides the line OA in the ratio 2 : 1 and M is the midpoint of the line OD.

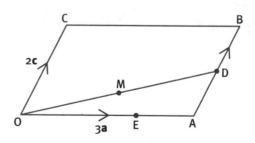

a) Express in terms of **a** and **c**:

  i) $\overrightarrow{OE}$ .... ①

  ii) $\overrightarrow{OD}$ .... ②

  iii) $\overrightarrow{OM}$ .... ①

  iv) $\overrightarrow{EC}$ .... ②

b) Prove that M lies on the line EC and that EM : MC = 1 : 3.

  ....

  .... ④

TOTAL 10

28 Here is a sketch of a triangle.

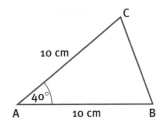

Anna was asked to make an accurate drawing of the triangle.
She can only measure lengths accurately to ±1 mm and angles to ±1°.
What is the shortest possible length of the line BC?

....

....

....

....

....

.... ③

TOTAL 3

29 A policeman timed a car travelling along a 100 m section of road. The time taken was 6 seconds.

The length of the road was accurate to the nearest 10 cm, and the time was measured accurate to the nearest second.

What was the greatest speed the car could have been travelling at?

....

....

.... ③

TOTAL 3

30 A town has a population of 74 000, and covers an area of 6.4 km².
Calculate the population density of the town. Give your answer correct to 3 s.f.

....

.... ②

TOTAL 2

Shape, space and measures

31 Amy has bought a new house. She is going to make a lawn in the back garden.

Amy buys a box of 4 kg of grass seed.

The instructions on the box say 100 g of seed will cover between 1 square metre and 1.25 square metres.

Amy decides to make a circular lawn.

What is the radius of the largest lawn she can make? Give your answer correct to 2 s.f.

....

....

....

.... ③

TOTAL 3

32 A large circular sign is fixed into the ground at the entrance to a park.

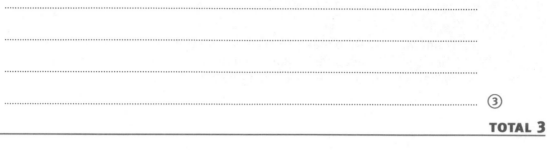

The shaded segment in the diagram shows the part of the sign that is below the surface of the ground.

The radius of the circle is 1.5 m. The chord AB is 2 m.

Calculate the area of the circle which is above the ground. Give your answer correct to 3 s.f.

....

....

....

....

....

.... ⑤

TOTAL 5

33 The shot put area on an athletics ground is a sector of a circle.
It is marked out in 5-metre intervals.

a) Calculate the length of the '5-metre' arc, AB.

....

.... ②

b) Calculate the area of the sector OCD.

....

.... ②

c) It is decided that the area of sector OCD is to be 100 m². What size will angle DOC have to be?

....

....

.... ②

TOTAL 6

Do not rub out your construction lines in questions 34 and 35.

34

The diagram is a scale drawing of a park.
1 cm represents 20 m.

The park has fences along each of the four sides, AB, BC, CD, DA.
There are gates at A, B, C, and D.

There is a children's play area which is more than 200 m from gate A and nearer to fence AB than to fence BC.

a)   On the diagram shade this area clearly and label it P.   ②

There is a quiet area which is more than 200 m from gate A and more than 120 m from fence AB.

b)   On the diagram shade this area and label it Q.   ②

A statue, S is 200 m from gate A and 120 m from fence AB.

c)   Mark S on the diagram.   ①

TOTAL 5

35 Two radar stations, A and B, are 150 km apart, with B due south of A.

Station A detects a ship S on a bearing of 146º and finds that the ship is within 100 km of B and nearer to B than A.

Using a scale of 1 cm to 20 km complete a drawing to show the position of the ship S. ③

TOTAL **3**

1 CX = CY; CA = CB (given)
∠C is common
∴△CXB ≡ △CYA (SAS) ②

2 DZ = DV + VZ
CV = CZ + VZ
∴DZ = CV
△DXC is isosceles (DX = XC, given)
∴∠BDZ = ∠ACV
∴∠XAB = ∠XCD (alternate)
and ∠ABX = ∠XDC (alternate)
∴△AXB is isosceles
∴AX = XB
∴DB = AC
So △DBZ ≡ △CAV (SAS) ③

3 a) $a = 10$ cm, $b = 6$ cm, ②
b) $x = 63°$, $y = 32°$, $z = 63°$ ③

4 a) i) ∠BAX = ∠XCD (alternate)
∠ABX = ∠CDX (alternate)
AB = DC (given)
∴△ABX ≡ △CDX (ASA) ③
ii) similar proof for △s ADX and CBX ②
b) DX = XB (△s AXB and CXD congruent)
AX = XC (△s ABX and CDX congruent)
∴X is midpoint of DB and AC.
DC = CB (ABCD is a rhombus)
∴∠XDC = ∠XBC (△BDC isosceles)
XC is common
∴△DXC ≡ △BXC
∴∠DXC = ∠BXC.
Since DB is a straight line
∠DXC = ∠BXC = 90° ③

5 105° ②

6 ∠DCB = ∠DCA (CD bisects ∠ACB)
∠DCA = ∠CAE (alternate)
∠DCB = ∠AEC (corresponding)
∴∠AEC = ∠CAE
∴△ACE is isosceles and AC = CE ③

7 $x = 26°$, $y = 22°$, $z = 48°$ ③

8 ∠DCB = 80° (sum of angles of quadrilateral is 360°)
∴∠ACB = 40° (AC bisects ∠DCB)
∴∠CAB = 180° − (40° + 70°) = 70°
∴△CAB is isosceles. ③

9 7.81 ②

10 a) 45 km   b) 51 km ④

11 $(l + 2)^2 = l^2 + 8^2$
$l = 15$ cm ③

12 a) 268 m   b) 18.5°   c) 51.3°
d) 624 m   e) 23.2° ⑤

13 a) Draw radius from P to meet tangent AB at X at right angles.
△AXP is isosceles, so AX = XP = r
$AP^2 = r^2 + r^2 = 2r^2$; $AP = r\sqrt{2}$ ③
b) $AC = 10\sqrt{2}$, $PQ = r + 2$, $QC = 2\sqrt{2}$ ③
c) $AC = AP + PQ + QC$
$10\sqrt{2} = r\sqrt{2} + r + 2 + 2\sqrt{2}$
$10\sqrt{2} = (r + 2)(\sqrt{2} + 1)$
$r = \dfrac{8\sqrt{2} - 2}{\sqrt{2} + 1}$ ④

14 a) 10.3 cm   b) 47° ④
c) ∠AOC = 60° (angle at centre = 2 × angle at circumference) and AO = OC (radii)
∴△AOC is equilateral ②
d) 43° ②

15 2170 m to 3 s.f. ④

Shape, space and measures

16 AS = AP, BP = BQ, CQ = CR, DR = DS
(tangents from same point are equal)
AB + CD = AP + PB + CR + RD
$\qquad$ = AS + BQ + CQ + DS
$\qquad$ = BC + DA ❹

17 a) i) 32° (angle in alternate segment) ❶
$\qquad$ ii) 40°   iii) 36° ❷
b) 7.4 cm ❸

18 95° ❸

EXAMINER'S TIP

Find the angles BDC, BCA using 'angles in the same segment'. Angle BPC is an exterior angle to triangle PDC.

19 a) 2.5 cm ❶
b) i) 5 cm ❶   ii) 1.82 cm ❷   iii) 5.72 cm ❷

20 a) i) 36 000 cm³ ❶   ii) 7200 cm² ❸
b) i) 88 574 cm³ ❷   ii) 13 122 cm² ❷

EXAMINER'S TIP

Remember ratio of areas = (ratio of lengths)² etc.

21 Area iii), vi)   Volume ii), v) ❸

22 a) reflection in the line $x + y = 0$ ❷
b) rotation 90° clockwise about the origin ❷
c) i) −2   ii) (1, 5) ❷

EXAMINER'S TIP

In part c) remember to join corresponding vertices with straight lines.

23 a) B, C and A ❶
b) reflection in the line COR ❷
c) i) rotation of 120° clockwise about O ❷
$\qquad$ ii) A ❶
d) i) C   ii) B ❷

EXAMINER'S TIP

In part c) it might be easier to think of the transformation that maps R onto Q and see what effect that has on point B.

24 14.8 cm³ ❷

25 85° ❶   13.3 cm ❶   31.48 cm³ ❷

26 a) i) $-\mathbf{a} + 2\mathbf{b}$ ii) $\frac{1}{2}(-\mathbf{a} + 2\mathbf{b})$
$\qquad$ iii) $\frac{1}{2}(\mathbf{a} + 2\mathbf{b})$ iv) $\frac{3}{4}(\mathbf{a} + 2\mathbf{b})$ ❹
b) O, E and F are on the same straight line
$\qquad$ $OE = \frac{2}{3}OF$ ❷

EXAMINER'S TIP

Take care with signs – be consistent with direction.

27 a) i) $2\mathbf{a}$ ❶   ii) $3\mathbf{a} + \mathbf{c}$ ❷   iii) $\frac{1}{2}(3\mathbf{a} + \mathbf{c})$ ❶
$\qquad$ iv) $2(\mathbf{c} - \mathbf{a})$ ❷
b) $\overrightarrow{EM} = \overrightarrow{EO} + \overrightarrow{OM}$
$\qquad$ $= -2\mathbf{a} + \frac{1}{2}(3\mathbf{a} + \mathbf{c})$
$\qquad$ $= -\frac{1}{2}(\mathbf{c} - \mathbf{a})$
$\overrightarrow{MC} = \overrightarrow{MO} + \overrightarrow{OC}$
$\qquad$ $= -\frac{1}{2}(3\mathbf{a} + \mathbf{c}) + 2\mathbf{c}$
$\qquad$ $= \frac{3}{2}(\mathbf{c} - \mathbf{a})$
Hence E, M and C lie on the same straight line and $EM : MC = \frac{1}{2} : \frac{3}{2}$
$\qquad\qquad\qquad = 1 : 3$ ❹

EXAMINER'S TIP

Take care with signs – be consistent with direction

28 6.6 cm ❸

29 19.1 m/s ❸

30 11 600 people per km² ❷

31 4.0 m ❸

32 6.54 m² ❺

EXAMINER'S TIP

Calculate area of sector AOB and area of triangle AOB.

33 a) 5.24 m   b) 118 m²   c) 51° ❻

34 ❺

32
❸

Shape, space and measures

Handling data

To revise this topic more thoroughly, see Chapter 4 in *Letts Revise GCSE Mathematics Study Guide*.

Try this sample GCSE question and then compare your answers with the Grade C and Grade A model answers on the next page.

People often buy Christmas cards in charity shops. The table shows the money received by a charity shop for two months before Christmas. Note that the shop is only open six days a week.

Money received (£M)	Frequency	Money received (£M)	Frequency
$0 < M \leqslant 50$	30	$200 < M \leqslant 250$	1
$50 < M \leqslant 100$	8	$250 < M \leqslant 300$	1
$100 < M \leqslant 150$	3	$300 < M \leqslant 350$	2
$150 < M \leqslant 200$	3		

a Calculate an estimate of the mean amount received each week.

....

....

.... **[4]**

b Complete the cumulative frequency table and draw the cumulative frequency graph of the distribution.

Money received, (£M)	$\leqslant 0$	$\leqslant 50$	$\leqslant 100$	$\leqslant 150$	$\leqslant 200$	$\leqslant 250$	$\leqslant 300$	$\leqslant 350$
Cumulative frequency	0							

[4]

c Use your graph to find the median and quartiles of the distribution. Show your method clearly.

....

....

.... **[3]**

d Janet said the average amount for sales of cards is about £70.
Comment on her statement.

....

....

.... **[1]**

(Total 12 marks)

These two answers are at grades C and A. Compare which one your answer is closest to and think how you could have improved it.

GRADE C ANSWER

Usha

a $(50 \times 30 + 100 \times 8 + 150 \times 3 + 200$
$\times 3 + 250 \times 1 + 300 \times 1 + 325 \times 2) \div 61$ ✓✗
$= £74.59$ ✗

Lose one mark for not using the mid-point of each group.

Lose one mark for dividing by 61 (the number of days in 2 months) rather than by 48.

One mark for the correct values.

b the missing cumulative frequency values are: 30, 38, 41, 44, 45, 46, 48 ✓

One mark for a correct division.

One mark for correctly drawing the axes and labelling the scales.

One mark for plotting the values correctly at the right-hand end of each group.

One mark for drawing a correct curve.

c Median = £30 ✓

lower quartile = £15 ✗

upper quartile = £45 ✗

No marks – mis-read scale? or no understanding of quartiles?

One mark – generous because there is no indication of how the median was found.

d the statement is true because it is close to the mean ✓

Although the mean has been calculated incorrectly the answer here is justified in relation to the answer to part a.

7 marks = Grade C answer

Grade booster ⋯⟩ move a C to a B

Usha needs to revise her understanding of how to calculate an estimate of the mean for grouped data. She also needs to be sure she knows how to find the quartiles and to practise reading values on scales.

GRADE A ANSWER

David

a $(25 \times 30 + 75 \times 8 + 125 \times 3 + 175 \times 3$
$+ 225 \times 1 + 275 \times 1 + 325 \times 2) \div 48$ ✓✓✓
$= £70.83$ ✓

Two marks for correctly using the mid-points to work out an estimate of the total and 1 mark for dividing by 48

Two marks for a correct answer

b the missing cumulative frequency values are: 30, 38, 41, 44, 45, 46, 48 ✓

One mark for the correct values.

One mark for correctly drawing the axes and labelling the scales,

One mark for plotting the values correctly at the right-hand end of each group,

One mark for drawing a correct curve.

Two marks for indicating how the median was found – drawing a line across at a cum freq of 24

similarly one mark here

and here.

Because there is no reason given, no mark is awarded.

(the statement is only true for the mean. If the median was used the statement would have said '... £35'. So the answer should, for example, be:

'true if the mean is considered'.

c Median is approx £35 ✓

lower quartile is approx £10 ✓

upper quartile is approx £85 ✓

d true

11 marks = Grade A answer

Grade booster ⋯⟩ move A to A*

David needs to appreciate that reasons, explanations and/or justifications must be given where asked for – and this includes justifying comments as in this question.

1 For each of the following situations describe the type of sampling being used.

a) From a list of names and addresses choosing the 5th, 15th, 25th, 35th name and so on

.... ①

b) When selecting 90 names from a list of 1800 names:

First generating a 4-digit random number on a calculator, e.g. 0.5247;

then multiplying this number by 1800, e.g. 944.46 and using the integer part e.g. 944 and choosing the 944th name and repeating this 90 times.

.... ①

c) Stopping 30 men and 30 women and asking them questions.

.... ①

TOTAL 3

2 A group of 800 people was asked for their views on a plan for a new bus station for a city. 450 people said they approved the plan.

a) 190 000 people live in the city.

Estimate the number of people in the city who would support the plan.

.... ②

b) If this is to be a reliable estimate what assumption must be made about the 800 people who were asked?

.... ①

TOTAL 3

3 Eddie, Bob and Amy are students at college. As part of a project they need to select a random sample of 50 students from the 1350 students at the college.

a) Eddie goes into college early and interviews the first 50 students he sees.

Explain why this might produce a biased sample.

....

.... ②

b) Bob lists all 1350 students in alphabetic order and selects every 15th on the list until he has chosen 50.

i) Explain why his sample is not random.

.... ②

ii) State if his sample is likely to be biased.

.... ①

c) Amy uses her calculator to generate 3-digit random numbers, such as 0.056 or 0.334.

Assuming that the number generated is always between 0 and 1, explain how Amy could use these numbers to select a random sample.

....

.... ②

TOTAL 7

4 Harry decides to investigate the weights of some chocolate bars to test the manufacturer's claim that all the bars weigh 70 g.

Harry buys 100 bars at the same time and from the same shop.

Comment on Harry's method of sampling.

.... ②

TOTAL 2

5 The manager of a supermarket wanted to estimate the number of people who visited his store in a town. He telephoned 100 people in the town one evening and asked 'Have you used the supermarket in the last week?'

13 people said they had, so the manager concluded that 13% of the town's population used his supermarket.

Give three criticisms of this method of estimation.

....

....

....

.... ③

TOTAL 3

6 The table shows the numbers of boys and the numbers of girls in Year 7 and Year 8 of a school

	Year 7	Year 8
Boys	100	50
Girls	90	60

The headteacher wants to find out what pupils think about wearing school uniform.

A stratified sample of 50 pupils is to be taken from Year 7 and Year 8.

Calculate the number of boys and the number of girls to be sampled from Year 7.

....

....

.... ②

TOTAL 2

7 Emily wants to do a survey as part of her statistics coursework. She has produced 30 questionnaires which she wants to give to pupils in each year.

The number of pupils in each year is given in the table below.

Year 7	Year 8	Year 9	Year 10	Year 11
140	140	100	100	120

Emily chooses to use a stratified sample.

How many students from each year should she sample?

....

....

....

....

....

.... ④

TOTAL 4

8 Janet is the manager of a charity shop. She records the daily takings for the shop in four-week blocks.

Table 1 below shows the takings for 2 four-week blocks.

Table 1 Shop takings in pounds

Week	1	2	3	4	1	2	3	4
Day								
Monday	136	140	146	145	145	139	149	165
Tuesday	153	159	168	175	171	194	186	132
Wednesday	146	139	135	150	139	158	164	170
Thursday	162	175	192	204	187	143	190	187
Friday	185	194	238	252	221	240	199	286
Saturday	220	232	275	315	265	270	334	392

a) Why might Janet consider using a 6-point moving average to present the data?

....

.... ①

The weekly totals are given below in Table 2, together with the first two calculations of the 4-point moving average.

b) Complete the column showing the 4-point moving averages, giving your answers correct to the nearest pound.

Table 2 Total and average takings, in pounds

Week	Total	Moving average
1	1002	
2	1039	
3	1154	1109
4	1241	1141
1	1128	——
2	1144	——
3	1222	——
4	1332	

③

The graph below shows the weekly totals.

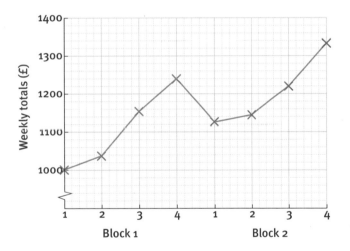

c) Plot the 4-point moving averages on the graph. ②

d) Comment on the general trend and the 4-weekly variation.

....

....

....

.... ③

TOTAL 9

Handling data

9 The table below shows the numbers of pairs of hiking boots sold by a sports shop during the period 1998–2000.

	Spring	Summer	Autumn	Winter
1998	43	17	15	15
1999	47	19	18	18
2000	57	26	22	13

a) Plot these figures on a graph, using a scale of 1 cm to each season (i.e. quarter) on the horizontal axis and 2 cm to 10 pairs of boots on the vertical axis. ④

b)   Complete the table below showing the 4-point moving average.

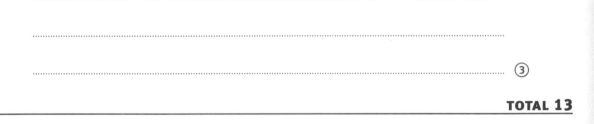

	Season	Total sold	Moving average
1998	Spring	43	
	Summer	17	
			22.5
	Autumn	15	
			23.5
	Winter	15	
1999			24.75
	Spring	47	
			25.5
	Summer	19	
			28.0
	Autumn	18	
			____
	Winter	18	
2000			____
	Spring	57	
			____
	Summer	26	
	Autumn	22	
	Winter	13	

③

c)   Plot the 4-point moving averages on the graph.   ③

d)   Comment on the general trend and the seasonal variation.

....

....

.... ③

TOTAL 13

Handling data

10 The table below shows the daily audiences for a production of 'An Inspector Calls' in a London theatre.

	Mon	Tues	Wed	Thurs	Fri	Sat
Week 1	250	318	330	446	570	610
Week 2	296	368	385	533	600	600
Week 3	240	335	325	500	565	583

a) Plot these figures on a graph. Use a scale of 1 cm for each day on the horizontal axis and 2 cm for 100 people on the vertical axis. ④

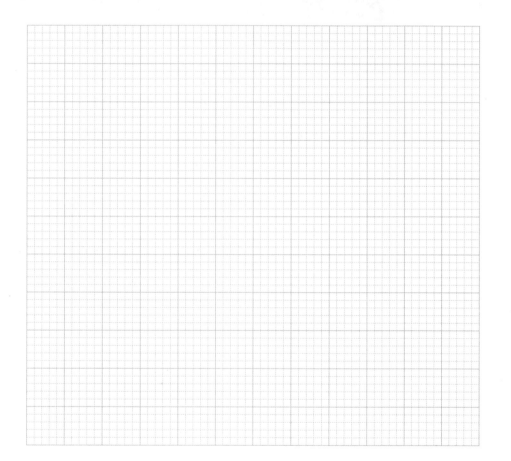

b) The table below has been used to calculate the 6-day moving averages, to the nearest whole number.

Calculate the last three entries for the table.

	Day	Audience	Moving average
Week 1	Monday	250	
	Tuesday	318	
	Wednesday	330	421
	Thursday	446	428
	Friday	570	437
	Saturday	610	446
Week 2	Monday	296	460
	Tuesday	368	465
	Wednesday	385	464
	Thursday	533	454
	Friday	600	449
	Saturday	600	439
Week 3	Monday	240	——
	Tuesday	335	——
	Wednesday	325	——
	Thursday	500	
	Friday	565	
	Saturday	583	

③

c) Plot the moving averages on the graph. ③

d) Comment on the general trend and the daily variation.

....

....

.... ③

TOTAL 13

Handling data

⑪ As part of a survey into shopping in a rural area, 200 people were asked to record the distances, in kilometres, from their homes to the Post Office.

The results are shown in the table.

Distance (x km)	Frequency
$0 < x \leqslant 5$	24
$5 < x \leqslant 10$	46
$10 < x \leqslant 15$	68
$15 < x \leqslant 20$	38
$20 < x \leqslant 25$	16
$25 < x \leqslant 30$	8

a) Write down the modal class.

.... ①

b) Calculate an estimate for the mean distance.

....

....

.... km ⑤

c) Complete the cumulative frequency table.

Distance (in km), less than or equal to	Cumulative frequency
5	24
10	70

③

d) Using a scale of 2 cm for 5 km on the horizontal axis and 1 cm for 10 people on the vertical axis draw a cumulative frequency curve to show this data.

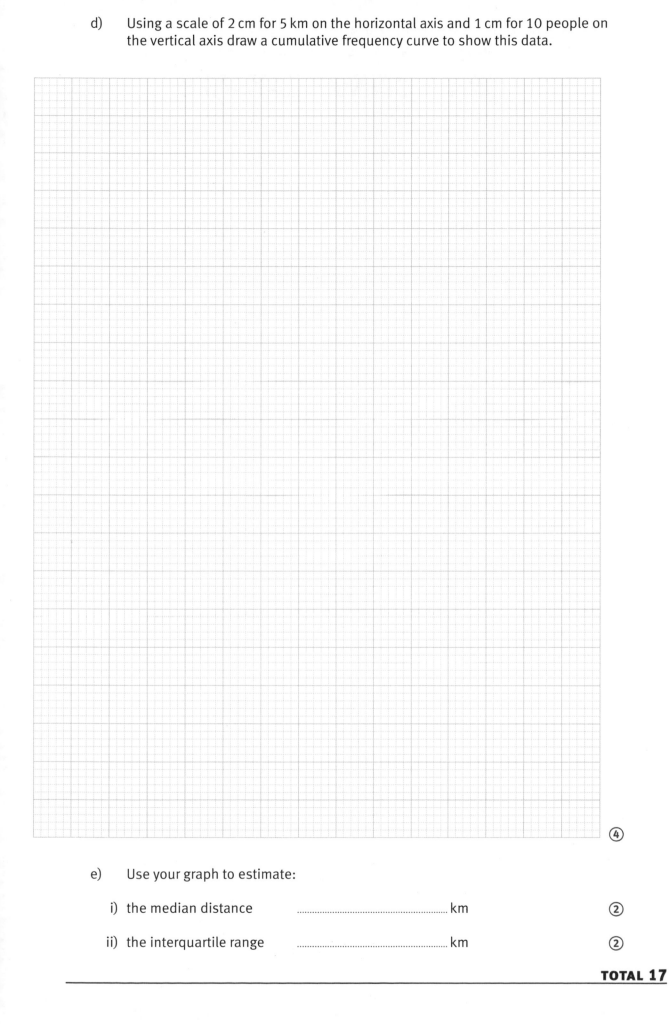

④

e) Use your graph to estimate:

i) the median distance .... km ②

ii) the interquartile range .... km ②

TOTAL 17

12 In a competition a total of 120 fish was caught.
The weights of the fish are summarised in the table below.

Weight (w g)	Frequency
$0 < w \leqslant 200$	12
$200 < w \leqslant 400$	34
$400 < w \leqslant 600$	48
$600 < w \leqslant 800$	20
$800 < w \leqslant 1000$	4
$1000 < w \leqslant 1200$	2

a) Calculate an estimate of the mean weight of the fish.

....

....

.... ④

b) Complete the cumulative frequency table.

Weight, (w g)	$w \leqslant 200$	$w \leqslant 400$	$w \leqslant 600$	$w \leqslant 800$	$w \leqslant 1000$	$w \leqslant 1200$
Cumulative frequency	12					

③

c) Draw the cumulative frequency graph for the weights of the fish.

d) Use your graph to find

i) the median .... g ①

ii) the interquartile range .... g ②

e) Estimate, correct to 1 d.p., the probability that a fish, picked at random, will weigh

i) less than 500 g

.... ①

ii) more than 750 g.

.... ①

TOTAL 16

13 The data shows the birth weights, in kilograms, of 20 babies.

2.4	2.7	3.2	2.5	3.1	1.9	3.5	4.0	2.7	4.0
4.1	2.8	4.2	3.4	1.6	4.2	3.8	2.6	3.0	2.4

a) Make a stem and leaf table, where 2 | 4 represents 2.4.

③

b) Find the median weight.

.... ①

TOTAL 4

14 A gardener measured the heights, in cm, of some trees four years after they had been planted. The results are shown below.

182	145	154	170	161	149	158	182
185	150	180	175	146	156	160	

a) Find the median and the quartiles.

....
....
.... ③

b) Draw a box and whisker plot.

③

TOTAL 6

15 As part of his coursework Alan found the reaction times for some students in his year.

The stem and leaf table below shows the data he obtained:

	males		females
2		2	4 4
2	2 2 2 2 3 3	2	2 2 3 3 3 3
2	0 1	2	0 0 1 1
1	8 8 8 8 9	1	8
1	6 7 7	1	7 7 7 7
1	4 4 5	1	4 4
1		1	
1		1	
0	8	0	

0|8 means 8 hundreths of a second, i.e. 0.08 secs

so 1|4 means 14 hundreths of a second, 0.140 secs

and 2|4 means 24 hundreths of a second, i.e. 0.240 secs.

There were 20 males and 19 females in Alan's experiment.

a) Find the median time for

   i) the males

   .... ①

   ii) the females.

   .... ①

b) Find the lower and upper quartiles for

   i) the males

   ....

   .... ②

   ii) the females.

   ....

   .... ②

c) Make two comparisons about the data.

....

....

.... ②

TOTAL 8

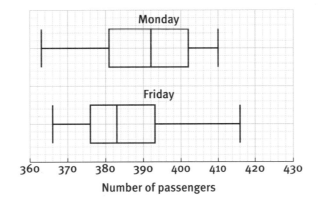

⑯ Susan works for a train company. Her job is to analyse the numbers of passengers who travel on the company's trains.

Susan compares the number of passengers who travel on the 0800 train to London on Mondays and on Fridays over a period of a year.

The box plots show her data.

Make two comments about the data.

....

.... ②

TOTAL 2

Handling data

17 As part of a primary school sports day 90 parents entered a three-legged egg and spoon race. The table summarises their times.

Time (t seconds)	Frequency
$10 \leqslant t < 20$	20
$20 \leqslant t < 30$	32
$30 \leqslant t < 40$	19
$40 \leqslant t < 60$	16
$60 \leqslant t < 90$	3
$t \geqslant 90$	0

a) Calculate an estimate of the mean time.

.... ④

b) Which class contains the median?

.... ②

c) Draw a histogram of the data on the grid below.

④

TOTAL 10

18 At Woodway Junior School 100 pupils took part in a challenge to build a large shape from different shaped and sized blocks.

Here are the times they took to complete the challenge.

Time (t seconds)	Number of pupils
$0 \leqslant t < 10$	0
$10 \leqslant t < 20$	9
$20 \leqslant t < 40$	20
$40 \leqslant t < 60$	30
$60 \leqslant t < 90$	15
$90 \leqslant t < 120$	6
$120 \leqslant t < 220$	20

a) Draw a histogram to show this information on the grid below. ④

After further practice the same 100 pupils were given a similar challenge to complete. Their times are shown in the histogram below.

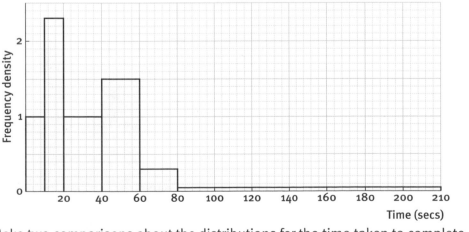

b) Make two comparisons about the distributions for the time taken to complete the challenge before and after practice.

.... ②

TOTAL 6

19 A college runs evening classes in different crafts such as cookery, pottery, art and woodwork.

The people who attend these evening classes are grouped into ages as shown in the table.

Age (x years)	Number of people
$20 \leqslant x < 25$	6
$25 \leqslant x < 30$	7
$30 \leqslant x < 40$	59
$40 \leqslant x < 50$	62
$50 \leqslant x < 60$	16
$60 \leqslant x < 80$	10

a) Complete the histogram below to show this distribution.

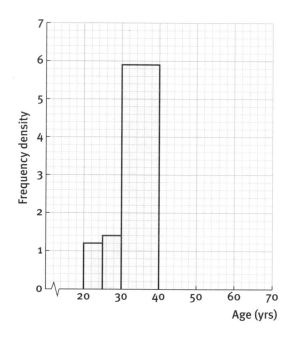

⑤

b) The principal of the college wishes to interview a sample of people who attend the evening classes. He decides to choose a stratifed random sample of 30 people. Show how this can be done.

....

....

....

.... ④

TOTAL 9

20 A poultry farmer takes a sample of 100 eggs laid by his hens.

The masses of the eggs are given in the table.

Mass (m g)	Frequency	Frequency density
$40 \leqslant m < 42$	3	
$42 \leqslant m < 46$	7	
$46 \leqslant m < 54$	28	
$54 \leqslant m < 62$	36	
$62 \leqslant m < 75$	26	

a) Use the table to calculate an estimate of the mean weight of the eggs.

....

.... ④

b) Calculate the frequency densities. ③

c) On the grid below, draw a histogram to show this data.

③

TOTAL 10

Handling data

21 Three numbers are represented by a, b and c where $b = a + 3$ and $c = b + 6$.

a) Write c in terms of a.

.... ②

b) Find the median of the three numbers.

.... ②

c) Find the mean of the three numbers.

....

.... ②

d) What is the difference between the mean and the median?

.... ②

TOTAL 8

22 A supermarket manager compared the times customers had to wait at his supermarket, 'Johnson's Supermarket,' and at a rival supermarket, 'Foods@Us'.

The times, in seconds, are summarised in the table below.

	Median	Lower quartile	Upper quartile	Minimum	Maximum
Johnson's	41	35	55	20	70
Foods@Us	45	30	60	25	68

a) Draw two box plots on the grid below to show this data.

③

b) Use the information to make three comparisons between the two supermarkets.

....

.... ③

The mean waiting times for each supermarket are:

Johnson's   48 seconds   *Foods@Us*   42 seconds

Here are two advertisements, one for each supermarket.

Johnson's

The average waiting time at our supermarket tills is

_____

Foods@Us

The average waiting time at our supermarket tills is

_____

c)   Which average waiting time would you use in these advertisements. Give reasons for your answer.

....

.... ②

TOTAL 8

23   A train operating company made a table showing how late 30 of its commuter trains were.

The data was available on this stem and leaf table. The times are in minutes.

2|4 means 24 minutes.

```
1 | 1 3 5 6
2 | 4 6 8 8 9
3 | 5 5 6 7 8
4 | 0 1 1 2 2 2 3 4 5 6 7 8
5 | 0 0 1 4
```

The company claimed 'on average, our trains were less than 38 minutes late'.

A commuters' organisation disagreed. They claimed the average time was 42 minutes.

Comment on these claims explaining what these times represented.

....

.... ④

TOTAL 4

24 a)   This bar chart shows the results of a test taken by 30 students.

i) How many students scored 7 marks?

.... ①

ii) Use the bar chart to complete the frequency table. ②

Mark	5	6	7	8	9
Frequency					

iii) Write down the mode.

.... ①

iv) Find the median.

.... ①

v) Calculate the mean.

.... ③

vi) Sally draws a pie chart to show the same information.
Calculate the angle she should use to show the number of students who scored 6 marks.

....

.... ②

12 boys and 8 girls take another test.
The mean mark of these 20 students is 7.

b) i) Calculate the total marks of these 20 students.

.... ①

ii) The mean mark of the boys is 6.5.
Calculate the mean mark of the girls.

....

....

.... ③

TOTAL 14

25 James is taking a test to become an apprentice with an engineering company.

The test consists of three parts.

The probability of James passing the numeracy test is 0.6.

The probability of him passing the literacy test is 0.7.

The probability of him passing the mechanical aptitude test is 0.4

a) Complete the tree diagram showing the possible outcomes of the three tests taken in the order given above.

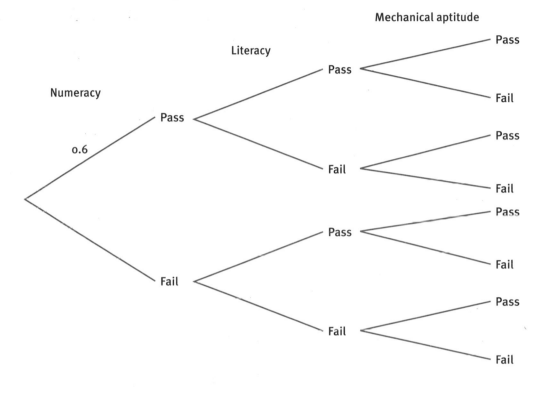

⑤

b) What is the probability that he will pass all three tests?

.... ③

c) If James passes two of the tests he is allowed to take the test he failed one more time.

What is the probability that he passes at least two of the tests?

.... ④

d) If James passes fewer than two tests he must repeat all three tests if he wishes to apply again. James is determined to become an apprentice.

What is the probability that he will have to repeat all three tests?

.... ②

TOTAL 14

26 The table shows the numbers of boys and the numbers of girls in Year 7 and
Year 8 of a school.

	Year 7	Year 8
Boys	100	50
Girls	90	60

The headteacher wants to find out what pupils think about the wearing of school
uniform.

He selects two pupils at random to interview, one pupil to be chosen from Year 7
and one pupil from Year 8.

a) Calculate the probability that both pupils will be boys.

.... ②

The headteacher decides to choose the 2 pupils at random from Year 7 and
Year 8 together.

b) i) Calculate the probability that both pupils will be boys.

.... ②

ii) Calculate the probability that both pupils will be from different Year groups.

.... ③

TOTAL 7

27 Brian makes a 7-sided spinner as shown.

a) If Brian spins it once the probability that he

i) gets the letter E is .... ①

ii) does not get the letter U is .... ①

iii) gets a letter from the word SUCCESS is .... ②

b) If he spins it 100 times about how many times should Brian expect to get the
letter U or K?

....

.... ④

Brian spins the spinner 700 times and his results are shown in the frequency
table.

Result	L	E	T	S	U	K
Frequency	70	91	287	98	78	76

c) i) Do you think Brian's spinner is biased? Give a reason for your answer.

.... ②

ii) Find the relative frequency of the outcome being U or K.

.... ②

iii) The spinner is spun another 140 times. Predict the number of times the letter L is likely to occur.

.... ②

TOTAL 14

28 In a game, discs numbered from 1 to 100 are picked at random from a bag and not replaced. The numbers picked are crossed off on cards.

Bob and Sheila are playing with one card each.

No number appears on both cards.

2		33	50	71	
5	19	37		73	95
	26		65	79	
8	29	46		85	99

Bob's Card

11	30		74	91	
4		34	63	77	94
7	25	47		80	
9		49	69		98

Sheila's Card

a) What is the probability that the first number picked is:

i) one of the numbers on Bob's card?

.... ②

ii) one of the even numbers on Sheila's card?

.... ②

iii) one of the numbers on Bob's card or on Sheila's card?

.... ②

b) What is the probability that the first number picked is on Bob's card and the second number picked is on Sheila's card?

.... ②

c) What is the probability that the first two numbers picked are even numbers both on Bob's card **or** both on Sheila's card **or** one on each card?

.... ⑤

TOTAL 13

Handling data

Handling data

1 a) systematic ❶
b) random ❶
c) quota ❶

2 a) 106 875 ❷
b) assume that the sample is representative ❶

3 a) E.g. students might all come from the same area by bus, or they might belong to an athletics club and come for training ❷
b) i) not all students equally likely to be selected ❷
ii) not biased as position in alphabet is not important ❶
c) number students from 1 to 1350 and multiply each random number by 1000 or by 1350 to produce a 1-, 2- or 3-digit number ❷

4 All the bars in the sample were likely to have been made at the same time – therefore may not be representative. ❷

5 E.g.
- only those with phones contacted ❶
- excludes people from outside the town ❶
- excludes those who perhaps only shop there once every 2 weeks ❶

6 $\frac{100}{300} \times 50 = 17$ boys, $\frac{90}{300} \times 50 = 15$ girls ❷

7 For Year 7 and Year 8 $\frac{140}{600} \times 30 = 7$ ❷

For Year 9 and Year 10 $\frac{100}{600} \times 30 = 5$ ❶

For Year 11 $\frac{120}{600} \times 30 = 6$ ❶

8 a) E.g. It would show the daily variation or trend over time ❶
b) moving averages are: £1167; £1184; £1207 ❸
c)

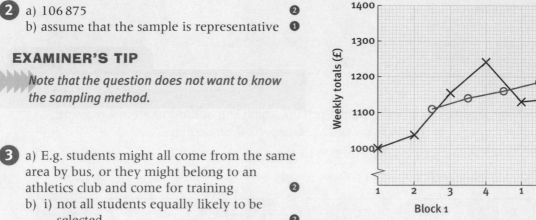

❷

d) E.g.
- takings are lower in the first week of each block
- takings rise steadily in weeks 2–4
- general trend is upwards ❸

9 a) see black graph line

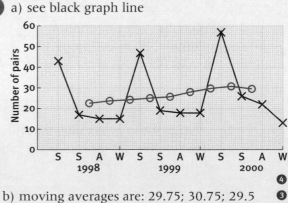

❹

b) moving averages are: 29.75; 30.75; 29.5 ❸
c) see red graph line ❸
d) E.g.
- general trend is upwards – but a slight decrease at the end
- always much higher in the first quarter i.e. in spring ❸

10 a) see black graph line

4

b) moving averages are 433, 428, 425 **3**

c) see red graph line **3**

d) E.g.
  - general trend upwards initially then downwards
  - Monday audience is always less than Friday or Saturday
  - attendance rises through the week
  - Saturday numbers always high **3**

EXAMINER'S TIP

Remember to plot the moving averages at the mid-point of each time period.

11 a) $10 < x \leqslant 15$ **1**

b) 12.5 km **5**

c)

Distance (in km), less than or equal to	Cumulative frequency
5	24
10	70
15	138
20	176
25	192
30	200

3

d)

e) i) 12 km **2**
   ii) 7.5 km **2**

EXAMINER'S TIP

Remember to use the mid-points of each group when calculating the mean distance.

12 a) 460 g **4**

b)

Weight (w g)	Cumulative frequency
$w \leqslant 200$	12
$w \leqslant 400$	46
$w \leqslant 600$	94
$w \leqslant 800$	114
$w \leqslant 1000$	118
$w \leqslant 1200$	120

3

c)

4

d) i) 450–500 g
   ii) 240–290 g

e) i) 0.52–0.53
   ii) 0.6–0.8 **4**

EXAMINER'S TIP

Remember at 750 g the cumulative frequency value is the number weighing 750 g or less, so you need the remainder who must weigh more than 750 g.

13 a)

0	
1	6 9
2	4 4 5 6 7 7 8
3	0 1 2 4 5 8
4	0 0 1 2 2

3

b) 3.05 kg **1**

EXAMINER'S TIP

Remember to order the values along each row.

14 a) Median = 160 **1**
   lower quartile = 150 **1**
   upper quartile = 180 **1**

b)

3

EXAMINER'S TIP

Remember to order the values along each row.

Handling data

15 a) Median times
    i) male = 18 hundreths i.e. 0.18 secs **❶**
    ii) female = 21 hundreths, i.e. 0.21 secs **❶**
  b) i) Males – upper quartile = 0.22 secs,
      lower quartile = 0.165 secs **❷**
    ii) Females – upper quartile = 0.23 secs,
      lower quartile = 0.17 secs **❷**
  c) E.g.
    • males times are more spread out – the range is greater
    • males generally have quicker reaction times **❷**

EXAMINER'S TIP

Remember to order the values along each row.

16 E.g.
  • The range for Monday $(410 - 363)$ is less than for Friday $(416 - 366)$.
  • The interquartile range for Monday is greater than for Friday.
  • The median number is greater on Monday.
  • 75% of the trains on Monday carry over 381 passengers while on Friday 75% of the trains carry over 376 passengers. **❷**

EXAMINER'S TIP

Remember that each section of the box plot represents 25% of the data.

17 a) 31 s **❹**
  b) $20 \leqslant t < 30$ **❷**
  c) Check your graph – the column heights should be as shown in this table:

Time (t seconds)	Height
$10 \leqslant t < 20$	2
$20 \leqslant t < 30$	3.2
$30 \leqslant t < 40$	1.9
$40 \leqslant t < 60$	0.8
$60 \leqslant t < 90$	0.1
$t \geqslant 90$	0

❹

EXAMINER'S TIP

Remember to calculate the frequency density.

18 a) Check your graph, the column heights should be as shown in this table:

Time (t seconds)	Height
$0 \leqslant t < 10$	0
$10 \leqslant t < 20$	0.9
$20 \leqslant t < 40$	1
$40 \leqslant t < 60$	1.5
$60 \leqslant t < 90$	0.5
$90 \leqslant t < 120$	0.2
$120 \leqslant t < 220$	0.2

❹

b) E.g.
  • wider range of times after practice
  • times decreased after practice
  • the distribution is skewed to the left after practice
  • the modal time is decreased **❷**

EXAMINER'S TIP

Remember to calculate the frequency density.

19 a) The frequency densities are:

Age (x years)	Frequency density
$20 \leqslant x < 25$	1.2
$25 \leqslant x < 30$	1.4
$30 \leqslant x < 40$	5.9
$40 \leqslant x < 50$	6.2
$50 \leqslant x < 60$	1.6
$60 \leqslant x < 80$	0.5

❸

check your graph; if correct then **❷**

b)

Age (x years)	Sample
$20 \leqslant x < 25$	1
$25 \leqslant x < 30$	1
$30 \leqslant x < 40$	11
$40 \leqslant x < 50$	12
$50 \leqslant x < 60$	3
$60 \leqslant x < 80$	2

❹

EXAMINER'S TIP

Part b) doesn't depend on a correct answer to part a).

20 a) 57 g **❹**

b)

Mass (m g)	Frequency density
$40 \leqslant m < 42$	1.5
$42 \leqslant m < 46$	1.75
$46 \leqslant m < 54$	3.5
$54 \leqslant m < 62$	4.5
$62 \leqslant m < 75$	2

❸

c) Correct histogram: check heights = frequency densities above **❸**

21 a) $c = (a + 3) + 6 = a + 9$ **❷**
  b) $a + 3$ **❷**
  c) Total $= a + (a + 3) + (a + 9) = 3a + 12$.
    Mean $= \dfrac{3a + 12}{3} = a + 4$ **❷**
  d) 1 **❷**

EXAMINER'S TIP

Take care when dividing by 3 in part c).

22 a)

b) E.g.
- The interquartile range for Johnson's is less.
- 50% of customers wait 41 seconds or less at Johnson's compared with 45 seconds or less at Foods@Us.
- The median for Johnson's is less than for Foods@Us.
- The range for Johnson's is greater than the range for Foods@Us.

 [**❸** for any three from the list]
c) Johnson's should use the median
 Foods@Us should use the mean **❷**

EXAMINER'S TIP

Remember that each section of the box plot represents 25% of the data.

23 Median = 40.5 minutes; Mean = 36.6 minutes; Mode = 42 minutes. E.g. the company are correct if they use and state that they are using the mean; the commuters are correct if they quote the mode – the most common. [**❷** for calculating the mean, **❶** for finding the mode, **❶** for the comment]

24 a) i) 5 **❶**
 ii) frequencies are: 10, 8, 5, 4, 3 **❷**
 iii) 5 marks **❶**
 iv) 6 **❷**
 v) 6.4 **❸**
 vi) 96° **❷**
 b) i) 140 **❶** ii) 7.75 **❸**

EXAMINER'S TIP

Use the answer for b) i) and the total mark for the boys to calculate b) ii)

25 a)

b) $0.6 \times 0.7 \times 0.4 = 0.168$ **❸**
c) PPP + PPF + PFP + FPP = $0.168 + 0.252 + 0.072 + 0.112 = 0.604$ **❹**
d) $1 - 0.604 = 0.396$ **❷**

EXAMINER'S TIP

in part c) be systematic so you don't miss a case.

26 a) $\frac{100}{190} \times \frac{50}{110} = \frac{50}{209} = 0.239$ **❷**
b) i) $\frac{150}{300} \times \frac{149}{299} = \frac{149}{598} = 0.249$ **❷**
 ii) $2 \times \frac{190}{300} \times \frac{110}{299} = \frac{418}{897} = 0.466$ **❸**

EXAMINER'S TIP

In part b) i) and ii) remember that the second probability involves one less in the total.

27 a) i) $\frac{1}{7}$ **❶**
 ii) $\frac{6}{7}$ **❶**
 iii) $\frac{3}{7}$ **❷**
b) 28 or 29 **❹**
c) i) Yes – the number of Ts is more than double the other results. **❷**
 ii) $\frac{78+76}{100} = 0.22$ **❷** iii) $\frac{70}{700} \times 140 = 14$ **❷**

EXAMINER'S TIP

In part c) i) remember to give reasons for your answer.

28 a) i) $\frac{17}{100}$ **❷**
 ii) $\frac{7}{100}$ **❷**
 iii) $\frac{17}{100} + \frac{17}{100} = \frac{34}{100} = \frac{17}{50}$ **❷**
b) $\frac{17}{100} \times \frac{17}{99} = \frac{289}{9900} = 0.029$ **❷**
c) $BB = \frac{5}{100} \times \frac{4}{99}$ $SS = \frac{7}{100} \times \frac{6}{99}$ $BS = \frac{5}{100} \times \frac{7}{99}$
 $SB = \frac{7}{100} \times \frac{5}{99} = \frac{132}{9900} = 0.013$ **❺**
 [**❶** for each correct fraction + **❶** for correct total]

EXAMINER'S TIP

In part c) be systematic – as the answer indicates.

Handling data

Formulae sheet: Higher tier

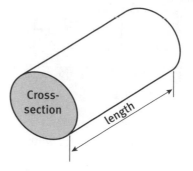

Volume of prism = (area of cross section) × length

In any triangle ABC

Sine rule $\dfrac{a}{\sin A} = \dfrac{b}{\sin B} = \dfrac{c}{\sin C}$

Cosine rule $a^2 = b^2 + c^2 - 2bc \cos A$

Area of triangle $= \dfrac{1}{2} ab \sin C$

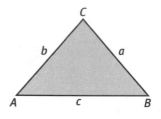

Volume of sphere $= \dfrac{4}{3} \pi r^3$

Surface area of sphere $= 4\pi r^2$

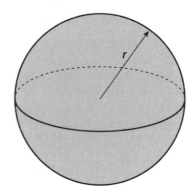

Volume of cone $= \dfrac{1}{3} \pi r^2 h$

Curved surface area of cone $= \pi r l$

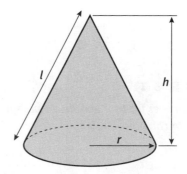

The Quadratic Equation

The solution of $ax^2 = bx + c = 0$ where $a \neq 0$, area given by $x = \dfrac{-b \pm \sqrt{(b^2 - 4ac)}}{2a}$

Letts **Examining Group**

General Certificate of Secondary Education

Mathematics
Paper 1

Higher tier

Time: two hours

Instructions to candidates

Write your name, centre number and candidate number in the boxes at the top of this page.

Answer ALL questions in the spaces provided on the question paper.

Show all stages in any calculations and state the units. **You must not use a calculator in this paper**.

Include diagrams in your answers where this may be helpful.

Information for candidates

The number of marks available is given in brackets **[2]** at the end of each question or part question.

The marks allocated and the spaces provided for your answers are a good indication of the length of answer required.

For Examiner's use only	
1	
2	
3	
4	
5	
6	
7	
8	
9	
10	
11	
12	
13	
14	
15	
16	
Total	

Letts
EDUCATIONAL

1   **(a)** Write 30 as a product of prime factors.

....

.... **[2]**

(b) Find **(i)** the LCM   **(ii)** the HCF of 30 and 54.

....

....

.... **[2]**

(Total 4 marks)

2   Mark and Brian drove to Cambridge. Mark took $2\frac{3}{4}$ hours. Brian's journey was $3\frac{1}{6}$ hours.

Work out

(a) $2\frac{3}{4} + 3\frac{1}{6}$

....

....

.... **[3]**

(b) $3\frac{1}{6} - 2\frac{3}{4}$

....

.... **[3]**

(Total 6 marks)

3   In a sale, prices were reduced by 20%. A suit in the sale cost £160.

Calculate the original price.

SALE
Everything reduced
20%

....

....

.... **[3]**

(Total 3 marks)

4 In each case, make c the subject of the formula.

(a) $y = mx + c$

....

.... **[1]**

(b) $e = mc^2$

....

....

.... **[2]**

(c) $a = \dfrac{bc - 4}{2c}$

....

....

.... **[2]**

(Total 5 marks)

5 In triangle ABC, DE is parallel to BC. AE = ED = DB = 3 cm, BC = 9 cm.

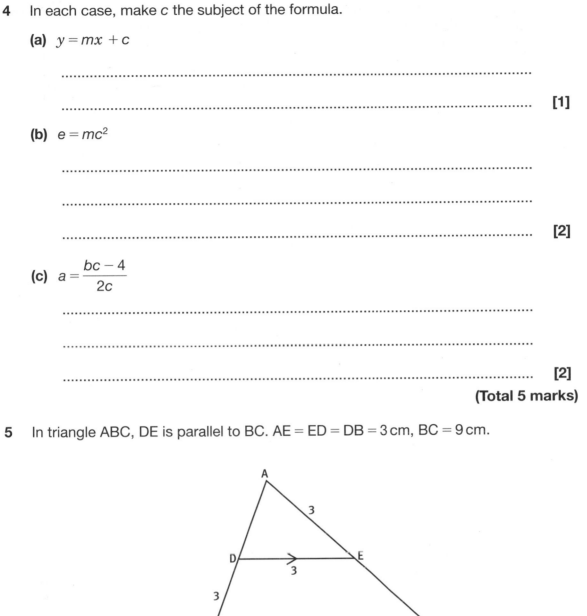

Find the lengths of:

(a) EC

....

....

.... **[2]**

(b) AD.

....

....

.... **[2]**

(Total 4 marks)

[turn over

Letts

6 A test is conducted to find out how long torch batteries last.
A sample of 100 *Britelite* batteries is tested. The results are shown on the
cumulative frequency diagram.

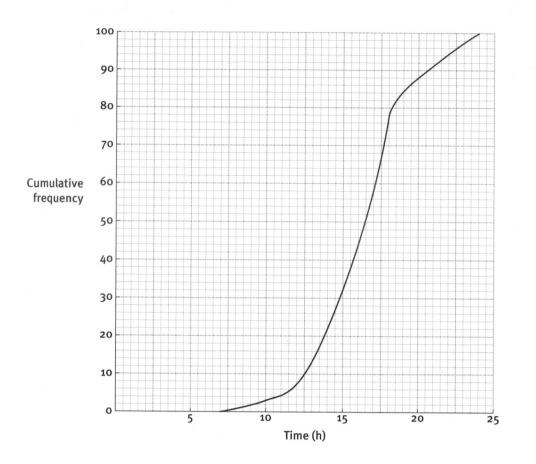

This table shows the results for a sample of 100 *Durabat* batteries.

Life (*L* hours)	Frequency
At least 10	1
$10 < L \leqslant 12$	5
$12 < L \leqslant 14$	27
$14 < L \leqslant 16$	42
$16 < L \leqslant 18$	20
$18 < L \leqslant 20$	5

(a) Draw a cumulative frequency diagram for *Durabat* on the same axes.

....

.... **[4]**

(b) Draw box plots for both samples.

....

....

.... **[5]**

(c) Compare the results for the two types of battery.

....

....

.... **[1]**

(Total 10 marks)

[turn over

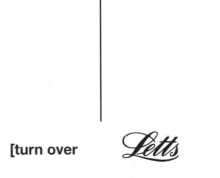

7   (a) Express $2x^2 + 5x - 3$ in factors.

....

....

....   **[2]**

(b) Hence solve

(i) $2x^2 + 5x - 3 = 0$

....

....

....   **[1]**

(ii) $2x^2 + 5x - 3 \leqslant 0$

....

....

....   **[2]**

(Total 5 marks)

8   (a) Solve this equation.

$$\frac{3x}{4} = 12$$

....

....

....   **[2]**

(b) Solve these simultaneous equations algebraically.

$$2x + 3y = -3$$
$$3x - 2y = 8\tfrac{1}{2}$$

....

....

....   **[4]**

(Total 6 marks)

Letts

9 ABCD is a parallelogram

A ———— B
D ———— C

(a) Prove that triangle ACD is congruent to triangle CAB.

....

....

.... **[3]**

(b) Describe a transformation that could also be used to demonstrate that these two triangles are congruent.

....

.... **[3]**

(Total 6 marks)

10 Two sets of traffic lights are connected.
The first set is green when you arrive
with probability 0.6.
If the first set is green the probability
that the second set will also be green
when you arrive is 0.8.

If the first set was not green and you had
to stop, the probability that the second set
will not be green when you arrive is 0.7.

Mr Parsons drives through the traffic lights.

What is the probability that he has to stop exactly once?

....

....

....

....

....

.... **[4]**

(Total 4 marks)

[turn over

11 Simplify these expressions and write as surds in the form $a + b\sqrt{c}$ or $b\sqrt{c}$.

(a) $\sqrt{10} \times \sqrt{50}$

.... **[1]**

(b) $\sqrt{5}(1 + \sqrt{5})$

.... **[1]**

(c) $\dfrac{1 + \sqrt{5}}{1 - \sqrt{5}}$

....

....

.... **[3]**

(Total 5 marks)

12 This is the graph of

$$y = x^3 - 2x^2 + x - 1.$$

Use the graph to solve the following equations.

(a) $x^3 - 2x^2 + x - 1 = 0$

.... **[1]**

(b) $x^3 - 2x^2 + x = 0$

....

....

.... **[2]**

(c) $x^3 - 2x^2 + 2x - 2 = 0$

....

....

.... **[3]**

(d) $x^3 - 2x^2 + 1 = 0$

....

.... **[3]**

(e) Are there any more roots of the equation in part **(d)**? Explain.

....

.... **[2]**

(Total 11 marks)

[turn over

13 (a) Write as single fractions in their simplest forms.

(i) $\dfrac{x}{2} - \dfrac{2x+1}{3}$

....

.... **[2]**

(ii) $\dfrac{2}{x} - \dfrac{3}{2x+1}$

....

....

....

.... **[4]**

(b) Simplify these expressions.

(i) $\dfrac{x^2 - x}{x^2 - 1}$

....

....

.... **[3]**

(ii) $\dfrac{5a^2b \times b^3}{10a^3b^2}$

....

....

.... **[3]**

(Total 12 marks)

14 O is the centre of the circle through A, B and C.
TCS is the tangent to the circle at C.

Angle AOC = 124°.

(a) Find the size of angle ACT.
Give a reason for each step.

....

....

....

.... **[3]**

(b) Express the angles of triangle ABC in terms of x.

....

....

....

.... **[3]**

(Total 6 marks)

[turn over

15 This wine bottle contains 750 ml.
A mathematically similar bottle (half-bottle)
contains 375 ml.

The height of the 750 ml bottle is 32 cm.

Here are three statements.

(a) The height of the half-bottle is 16 cm.

(b) The height of the half-bottle is less than 16 cm.

(c) The height of the half-bottle is about 25 cm.

For each statement, say whether it is true and give a reason.

....

....

....

....

....

....

....

.... **[6]**

(Total 6 marks)

16 (a) On the diagram draw vectors **c** and **d**, where

$$c = a + 2b, \quad d = 2a + b.$$

[2]

The points A, B, C and D have position vectors **a**, **b**, **c** and **d**.

(b) Find $\overrightarrow{AD}$ in terms of **a** and **b**.

....

.... **[2]**

(c) Hence prove that ABCD is a parallelogram.

....

....

....

....

....

.... **[3]**

(Total 7 marks)

Letts Examining Group

General Certificate of Secondary Education

Mathematics
Paper 2
Higher tier

Time: two hours

Instructions to candidates

Write your name, centre number and candidate number in the boxes at the top of this page.

Answer ALL questions in the spaces provided on the question paper.

Show all stages in any calculations and state the units. You are expected to use a calculator in this paper.

Include diagrams in your answers where this may be helpful.

Information for candidates

The number of marks available is given in brackets **[2]** at the end of each question or part question.

The marks allocated and the spaces provided for your answers are a good indication of the length of answer required.

1 Use a trial and improvement method to find the value of x, correct to two decimal places, when

Leave blank

$$x^3 + x - 1 = 0$$

....

....

....

....

....

.... **[4]**

(Total 4 marks)

2 (a) Use your calculator to find the values of the following expressions.
Give your answers correct to two decimal places.

(i) $\dfrac{429 \times 0.93}{0.33 + 0.54}$

....

.... **[2]**

(ii) $\sqrt{0.63^3 + 0.63^2}$

....

.... **[2]**

(b) The distances of three planets from the Sun are:

Earth	1.5×10^8 km
Pluto	6.02×10^9 km
Mercury	5.8×10^7 km

The ratio:

Pluto's distance from the Sun : Earth's distance from the Sun $= 4.01 \times 10^1 : 1$

What is the corresponding ratio for Mercury and Earth?
Give your answer in standard form correct to three significant figures.

....

.... **[2]**

(Total 6 marks)

3 **(a)** Simplify

$$3(5m + 4) - 4(3m + 5)$$

.... **[2]**

(b) **(i)** Factorise

$$x^2 - 3x - 4$$

....

.... **[2]**

(ii) Solve this equation.

$$x^2 - 3x - 4 = 0$$

.... **[1]**

(Total 5 marks)

4 In 2001 Bob was quoted a basic car insurance premium of £1100 for one year.
Bob agreed to pay the first £500 of any claim and this meant he gained a 15% discount.
Because Bob had a 'no claim' bonus he also received a further 20% discount on the reduced premium.

(a) How much did Bob have to pay?

....

.... **[2]**

Bob decided to pay by 12 equal monthly instalments, but this added 10% to the reduced premium.

(b) How much did Bob pay each month?

....

.... **[2]**

For a different make of car, in 2002, Bob is quoted a basic insurance premium of £1500.
This was 15% more than the 2001 basic premium on this make of car.

(c) Find the value of the 2001 basic premium for this car. Round your answer to the nearest pound.

....

.... **[3]**

(Total 7 marks)

[turn over

5 **(a)** Bill and Tony work in the same office. They have a wager that they will come to work in the same colour of shirt one day.

Bill has 10 shirts: 4 white, 3 blue, 3 grey

Tony has 8 shirts: 2 white, 2 blue, 4 grey

What is the probability that they will wear the same colour shirt?

....

.... **[5]**

(b) Mike wears a clean shirt every day.

He also has 10 shirts: 6 white, 2 blue, 2 grey

Bill and Tony also wager that Mike will wear the same colour shirt for 3 consecutive days.

What is the probability that this will happen?

....

.... **[4]**

(Total 9 marks)

6 The diagram shows a solid bar of lead.
The bar is a prism. The cross-section of the prism is an isosceles trapezium.

(a) Calculate the volume of the bar.

....

.... **[4]**

(b) Given that the density of lead is 11.35 g/cm^3, calculate the mass of the bar.
Give your answer in kg correct to 3 significant figures.

....

.... **[1]**

(c) Calculate the area of the sloping face. Give your answer correct to
3 significant figures.

....

.... **[3]**

(d) Calculate the angle $x°$ which the sloping face makes with the base.

....

.... **[3]**

(Total 11 marks)

7 (a) Factorise

(i) $3x^2 + 15x$

.... **[2]**

(ii) $x^2 - 5x - 36$

....

.... **[2]**

(b) Simplify

$$\frac{m^3 p^4 \times m^2 p^5}{m^4 p^6}$$

....

.... **[2]**

(Total 6 marks)

[turn over

8   **(a)** On the grid below, using values of x from 0 to 6, draw the graphs of
$2x + 3y = 12$ and $3x - 2y = 3$.

[5]

     (b) Use your graph to solve the simultaneous equations

$$2x + 3y = 12$$
$$3x - 2y = 3$$

$x = $ ....; $y = $ ....   **[1]**

(Total 6 marks)

9   In this question $a = 2 - 3\sqrt{2}$.

     (a) Express a^2 in terms of $\sqrt{2}$ simplifying your answer as much as possible.

....

.... **[2]**

     (b) Hence show that $x = a$ is one solution of the equation

$$x^2 + 4x - 30 = 0$$

....

....

.... **[1]**

(Total 3 marks)

10 The diagram below shows a rectangle, A, length 11 cm and width y cm, and a square, S, side x cm.

(a) Write down an expression for the perimeter of

(i) the rectangle

.... **[1]**

(ii) the square.

.... **[1]**

The perimeter of the square and the rectangle are equal.

(b) Use this fact to write down an expression for y in terms of x.

....

.... **[2]**

The area of the square is 4 cm² more than the area of the rectangle.

(c) (i) Write down an equation satisfied by x and show that it simplifies to

$$x^2 - 22x + 117 = 0$$

....

....

.... **[2]**

(ii) Solve this equation, giving the two possible values of x.

....

.... **[3]**

(Total 9 marks)

119   [turn over   *Letts*

11 The time between 150 successive aircraft landing at a busy airport, during the period 0800–1400 one day, is given in the table. For example, on 24 occasions an aircraft arrived within 60 seconds of the aircraft in front of it.

Time t between aircraft (seconds)	Number of aircraft i.e. frequency
$0 \leqslant t < 60$	24
$60 \leqslant t < 120$	34
$120 \leqslant t < 180$	27
$180 \leqslant t < 300$	38
$300 \leqslant t < 420$	27

(a) Estimate the mean time between arrivals.

....

....

....

.... **[3]**

(b) On the grid below draw a histogram to show this data.

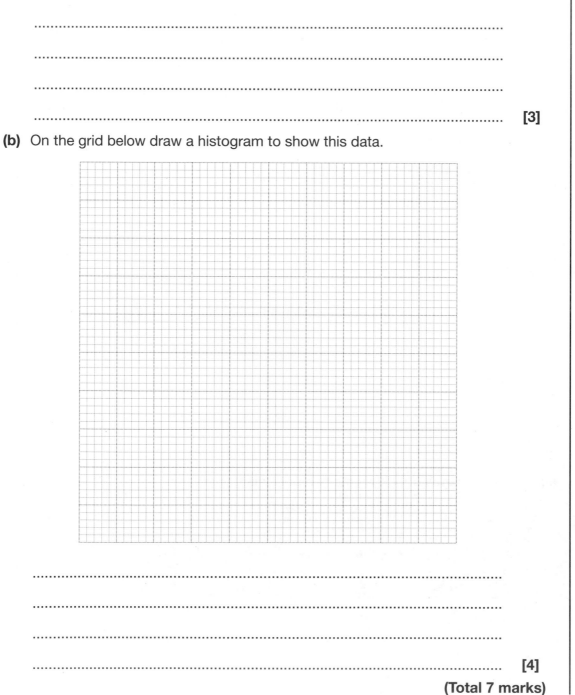

....

....

....

.... **[4]**

(Total 7 marks)

12 The pressure of the water, *P*, at any point below the surface of the sea varies as the depth, *D*, of that point below the surface.

The pressure is 400 newtons/cm^2 at a depth of 6 m.

Find the pressure at a depth of 20 m.

Give your answer correct to the nearest whole number.

Leave blank

....

....

....

.... **[3]**

(Total 3 marks)

13 A solid metal cone of height 100 cm and base radius 70 cm is melted down and recast as two identical solid cylinders of length 60 cm.

Calculate the radius of the cylinders.

100 cm

70 cm

60 cm

....

....

....

.... **[5]**

(Total 5 marks)

[turn over

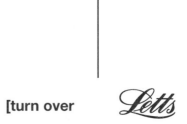

14 In the triangle ABC, AB = 10 cm, AC = 15 cm and angle BAC = $x°$.

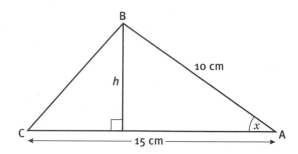

(a) Write down an expression for the height h in terms of x.

....

.... **[1]**

(b) Show that the area of triangle ABC is 75 sin x cm².

....

....

.... **[1]**

(c) If the area of triangle ABC is 50 cm², calculate the size of angle x.

....

....

.... **[2]**

The area of this obtuse-angled triangle PQR is also 50 cm².

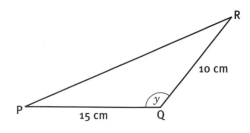

(d) Calculate the size of angle y.

....

....

.... **[1]**

Letts

(e) Calculate the length of PR.

....

....

.... **[4]**

(Total 9 marks)

15 The dimensions of the cuboid in the diagram below are accurate to the nearest cm.

6 cm

12 cm

10 cm

What is the difference between the greatest true volume and the least true volume? Give your answer correct to two decimal places.

....

....

....

.... **[3]**

(Total 3 marks)

16 Use algebra to solve the equation:

$$\frac{4}{x+3} - \frac{3}{x+4} = 1$$

....

....

....

....

....

.... **[7]**

(Total 7 marks)

[turn over

Answers to mock examination Paper 1

1 **(a)** $2 \times 3 \times 5$ [2]

(b) **(i)** 270 [1]

(ii) 6 [1]

2 **(a)** $5\frac{11}{12}$ [3]

(b) $\frac{5}{12}$ [3]

3 £200 [3]

4 **(a)** $c = y - mx$ [1]

(b) $c = \pm\sqrt{\dfrac{e}{m}}$ [2]

(c) $c = \dfrac{4}{b - 2a}$ [2]

5 **(a)** $EC = 3 \times 3 - 3 = 6$ [2]

(b) $AD = \frac{1}{2}DB = 1\frac{1}{2}$ [2]

6 **(a)**

[4]

(b) *Britelite* batteries

Durabat batteries

[5]

(c) Durabat last longer although a few failed early. [1]

7 **(a)** $(2x - 1)(x + 3)$ [2]

(b) **(i)** $x = \frac{1}{2}, -3$ [1]

(ii) $-3 \leqslant x \leqslant \frac{1}{2}$ [2]

8 **(a)** $x = 16$ [2]

(b) $x = 1\frac{1}{2}, y = -2$ [4]

9 **(a)** AD = CB (opposite sides of a parallelogram)
DC = BA (opposite sides of a parallelogram)
AC common
Triangles congruent (SSS)   [3]

(b) Rotation, half-turn about mid-point
of AC   [3]

EXAMINER'S TIP

*To describe a transformation be sure to include
all the details.*

10 $0.6 \times 0.2 + 0.4 \times 0.3 = 0.24$ [4]

EXAMINER'S TIP

You may find it helpful to draw a tree diagram.

11 **(a)** $10\sqrt{5}$ [1]
(b) $5 + \sqrt{5}$ [1]
(c) $-1\frac{1}{2} - \frac{1}{2}\sqrt{5}$ [3]

EXAMINER'S TIP

*Be careful with the signs in **(c)**.*

12 **(a)** Read at $y = 0$ (1.8 or 1.9)   [1]
(b) Read at $y = -1$ (0, 1 repeated)   [2]
(c) Read at $y = 1 - x$ (−0.5)   [3]
(d) Read at $y = x - 2$ (0.3, 2.85)   [3]
(e) Yes, one more off the diagram (left) as
cubic graph gets steeper.   [2]

EXAMINER'S TIP

*Draw the required lines ($y = -1$, $y = 1 - x$,
$y = x - 2$) on the graph.*

13 **(a)** **(i)** $-\dfrac{x+2}{6}$ [2]

(ii) $\dfrac{x+2}{x(2x+1)}$ [4]

(b) **(i)** $\dfrac{x}{x+1}$ [3]

(ii) $\dfrac{b^2}{2a}$ [3]

EXAMINER'S TIP

Show all the steps of your working.

14 **(a)** Angle ABC = 62° (angle at circumference
half angle at centre)

Angle ACT = 62° (angle in alternate
segment)

(or use isosceles triangle AOC)   [3]

(b) B = 62°, A = x, C = 90° − x + 28° = 118° − x.
   [3]

EXAMINER'S TIP

Make your reasons clear to earn the marks.

15 **(a)** False since volume scale factor is the cube
of the linear scale factor.   [2]

(b) False since cube root of $\frac{1}{2}$ is greater
than $\frac{1}{2}$.   [2]

(c) True, $\frac{32}{25} = 1.28$ and $1.28^3 \approx 2$ [2]

EXAMINER'S TIP

*This is about using the volume scale factor and
giving reasons.*

16 **(a)**

   [2]

(b) $\overrightarrow{AD} = 2\mathbf{a} + \mathbf{b} - \mathbf{a} = \mathbf{a} + \mathbf{b}$ [2]

(c) $\overrightarrow{BC} = \mathbf{a} + 2\mathbf{b} - \mathbf{b} = \mathbf{a} + \mathbf{b}$
$\overrightarrow{AD} = \overrightarrow{BC}$, opposite sides equal and
parallel   [3]

EXAMINER'S TIP

*It will still work if you take the letters in the
wrong order, $\overrightarrow{CB} = -(\mathbf{a} + \mathbf{b})$*

Answers to mock examination Paper 2

1 0.68 [4]

2 **(a)** **(i)** 458.59 [2]

  (ii) 0.80 [2]

  (b) $3.87 \times 10^{-1}:1$ [2]

3 **(a)** $3m - 8$ [2]

  (b) **(i)** $(x + 1)(x - 4)$ [2]

  (ii) $x = -1; x = 4$ [1]

4 **(a)** £748 [2]

  (b) £68.57 [2]

  (c) £1304 [3]

5 **(a)** $P(WW) = \frac{4}{10} \times \frac{2}{8} = \frac{1}{10}$

  $P(BB) = \frac{3}{10} \times \frac{2}{8} = \frac{3}{40}$

  $P(GG) = \frac{3}{10} \times \frac{4}{8} = \frac{3}{20}$

  $P(\text{same colour}) = \frac{1}{10} + \frac{3}{40} + \frac{3}{20} = \frac{13}{40}$ [5]

  (b) must be a white shirt,

  $P(W) = \frac{6}{10} \times \frac{5}{9} \times \frac{4}{8} = \frac{1}{6}$ or $0.16\dot{6}$ [4]

6 **(a)** $288 \, \text{cm}^3$ [4]

  (b) $3.27 \, \text{kg}$ [1]

  (c) $43.3 \, \text{cm}^2$ [3]

  (d) $56.3°$ [3]

7 **(a)** **(i)** $3x(x + 5)$ [2]

  (ii) $(x - 9)(x + 4)$ [2]

  (b) mp^3 [2]

8 **(a)**

[5]

  (b) $x = 2.5, y = 2.3$ [1]

9 **(a)** $2(11 - 6\sqrt{2})$ [2]

  (b) $(22 - 12\sqrt{2}) + 4(2 - 3\sqrt{2}) - 30$

  $= 22 - 12\sqrt{2} + 8 + 12\sqrt{2} - 30 = 0$ [1]

10 (a) (i) $2y + 22$ [1]

(ii) $4x$ [1]

(b) $y = 2x - 11$ [2]

(c) (i) $x^2 - 4 = 11(2x - 11)$ [2]

(ii) 13, 9 [3]

EXAMINER'S TIP

In (c) remember to subtract 4 from x^2 to equate with the area of the rectangle.

11 (a) 177.8 seconds [3]

(b) Frequency densities are 0.4, 0.57, 0.45, 0.32 and 0.23

[4]

EXAMINER'S TIP

Remember to use mid-interval values and calculate frequency density.

12 1333 N/cm^2 [3]

EXAMINER'S TIP

Because the question is concerned with proportionality you do not have to convert to cm or to m.

13 36.9 cm [5]

EXAMINER'S TIP

Remember the question is concerned with 2 cylinders.

14 (a) $10 \sin x$ [1]

(b) $A = \frac{1}{2}$ base $\times$ height
$= \frac{1}{2} \times 15 \times 10 \sin x$
$= 75 \sin x$ [1]

(c) 41.8° [2]

(d) 138.2° [1]

(e) 23.4 cm [4]

EXAMINER'S TIP

In (d) use the formula area of a triangle $= \frac{1}{2} ab \sin C$.

15 252.25 cm^3 [3]

EXAMINER'S TIP

Remember the difference is $(12.5 \times 10.5 \times 6.5) - (11.5 \times 9.5 \times 5.5)$

16 -5, or -1 [7]

EXAMINER'S TIP

Multiply through by $(x + 3)(x + 4)$ giving $4(x + 4) - 3(x + 3) = (x + 3)(x + 4)$ and solve this.

Index